Contents

Acknowledgements

We would like to thank our loving daughters Siân and Fran for 'bullying' us into writing this book and for their encouragement throughout. In addition, thanks are given to Mr Dennis Richards, Headteacher, and Dr Doug Wilford, Head of Science Faculty, at St Aidan's Church of England High School, Harrogate, for their support. Our thanks must also go to Katie Mackenzie Stuart, Julie Jones and the editorial staff at John Murray Publishers who made sense of our manuscript.

The Examination Boards

This book was written to cover all GCSE Biology syllabuses. The authors and publishers are grateful to the following examination boards for kind permission to reproduce past examination questions. The answers supplied are written by the authors. The examination boards have not approved the answers and bear no responsibility for their accuracy. The addresses given below are those of the examination boards from whom specific syllabuses can be obtained.

Welsh Joint Education Committee (WJEC),
245 Western Avenue,
Cardiff,
CF5 2YX

Northern Examinations and Assessment Board (NEAB),
Devas Street,
Manchester,
M15 6EX

Southern Examination Group (SEG),
Stag Hill House,
Guildford,
Surrey,
GU2 5XJ

Midland Examining Group (MEG),
Syndicate Buildings,
1 Hills Road,
Cambridge,
CB1 2EU

London Examinations, A division of EDEXCEL Foundation (London),
Stewart House,
32 Russell Square,
London,
WC1B 5DN

Northern Ireland Council for the Curriculum, Examinations and Assessment (NICCEA),
Clarendon Dock,
29 Clarendon Road,
Belfast,
BT1 3BG

Photo acknowledgements

The publishers are grateful to the following for permission to reproduce copyright photographs:
p.93 © Stephen Dalton/NHPA.

Introduction

During the last few years you have gained a great deal of important knowledge and understanding from the National Curriculum – Science (Biology). You have probably forgotten some of the work. This work must be revised and relearned for your examinations. Unfortunately, revision is hard work and it is easy to avoid. Some of the most common ways are shown in the cartoons below.

First, get organised!

Plan

It is always a good idea to plan your revision.

- Make a list of all the subsections you must revise.
- Now make a timetable.
- You must make sure you leave enough time to revise all the subsections.

The plan below is an example of a revision timetable. Each box represents 2 or 3 hours of work. There is one box for a school day, and two for the weekend and holiday days. Make up something like this for your own revision.

Study/Revision planner	Mon	Tues	Wed	Thurs	Fri	Sat am	Sat pm	Sun am	Sun pm
1 Plan all your revision before you begin it.	Section 1 1.1–1.3	Try exam questions	Section 2 2.1–2.2	Section 2 2.3–2.4	20 March	Section 2 2.5–2.6	Section 2 2.7–2.8	Try exam questions	Time off
2 Each box represents 2 or 3 hours work.	Section 2 2.9–2.10	Try exam questions	Section 3 3.1–3.2	etc	27 March				
3 Try to keep to your plan, but don't be afraid to change it.					3 April				
					10 April				

Be an active learner

Try to be an active learner. Don't just read your notes or this book. Tackle a subsection at a time. As you read your notes/this book do the following:

- Note down or underline key words of phrases.
- Make sure you can remember any diagrams and labels on the diagrams.
- Summarise the key points and use these to help you remember the details in your notes.
- Try to answer the quick questions and examination questions.
- Check your answers and then go over anything you are unsure about again.

Example of a revision summary:
e.g. subsection 2.6 Homeostasis

- Underline the definition of homeostasis, organs involved, key words such as ultrafiltration, selective reabsorption, dialysis, etc.
- Check that you can remember the names and positions of kidney, bladder, renal vein, renal artery, etc. on your diagrams.
- Summarise the key points about the kidney:
  - ultrafiltration – liquid part of the blood is filtered into the kidney tubule and large protein molecules stay in the blood capillaries
  - selective reabsorption – useful substances, e.g. glucose, amino acids and water, are reabsorbed back into the blood
  - water content is controlled by ADH
  - kidney failure means a person needs kidney dialysis
  - in a dialysis machine, blood and dialysis fluid move in opposite directions.
- Attempt all questions.
- If you cannot answer all the questions, revise the subsection again.

How to use this book!

This book has been written to help you prepare for your GCSE Biology examination – whether as separate Science: Biology, or as the Biology component of a Double Award (Coordinated) course.

This book will be of most use to you as you come to the end of your Biology course, especially when you are ready to start your revision. Of course this book can be useful in other ways, such as when you are preparing for tests or internal examinations during your GCSE course.

Your teacher will suggest which level you should aim for, foundation or higher. Also it is very important for you to obtain a copy of the syllabus you are studying from your teacher.

1 This book is written in seven sections each of which has been divided into subsections. They may not be in the same order that you are being taught. Work through each subsection and make sure you understand it and that you can answer all the questions before moving on.
2 The first time scientific terms are used they are printed in **bold**. These words and phrases are included in the glossary on pages 149–151. This glossary can be used as a self-test or as a simple reference section.
3 To help draw attention to key words and words/ phrases that should be included in examination answers, the first time these are used they are printed in SMALL CAPITALS.
4 Examination questions are given at the end of each section so you can test your knowledge and understanding of the work covered. The level of each question (foundation or higher) is indicated at the end of each question. Questions are from GCSE Science: Biology papers, unless it is stated 'Double Award' or 'Coordinated' at the end of the questions. Check your answers with those on pages 132–140 as you go along (see your teacher about anything you still do not understand).
5 You will need to work through each section as many times as you can. Each time, your knowledge and understanding will improve as you become more familiar with the work.

Section
ONE

Life processes
and
cell activity

1.1 Basic principles

Characteristics of living organisms

All living organisms are capable of:

- Respiration.
- Excretion.
- Feeding.
- Growth.
- Reproduction.
- Moving.
- Sensitivity.

Respiration is needed to release ENERGY. Every living cell of an organism, whether it is from the gut lining or from a seed that has been dormant for several years, must respire.

Excretion is necessary to remove unwanted chemicals from the body. These chemicals have been made in the body as a result of **metabolism**. You must not confuse these with:

1 Products of **egestion** (faeces), which have never been a part of the body – they have simply passed through it.
2 **Secretion** by the body of useful chemicals like saliva and tears.

Feeding occurs when animals eat other organisms to obtain their food, whereas plants can make their own food by photosynthesis using light energy.

Growth of offspring to adult size. In animals this is mainly by increasing cell number. In plants increase in cell number is accompanied by a huge increase in cell size as the cells take in large quantities of water.

Reproduction is essential for the continuation of the species. As all living organisms die, some must reproduce if the species is not to become extinct.

Movement can be by the whole organism or part of it. Sometimes this is the result of muscular action as in animals. Plants 'move' by growing towards or away from a stimulus such as light.

Sensitivity allows all organisms to be aware of what is happening in their environment; this is necessary if they are to survive. They must know when to hibernate, for example, or to move away from dangers such as predators.

The cell theory

This states that all living things are made of cells. Some animals and plants are made up of a single cell, for example *Amoeba*. Most cells have the following parts (see Figure 1.1.1):

1 NUCLEUS, which contains the hereditary material and controls the life of the cell.

2 CYTOPLASM, which is mainly water and is where most of the chemical reactions take place. It contains many organelles, the most important of which are the mitochondria involved in energy production.
3 CELL MEMBRANE, which controls movement of materials into and out of the cell.

Plant cells (Figure 1.1.2) also have a CELL WALL made of cellulose, which gives shape and rigidity to the cell. They often have a large central VACUOLE filled with a solution of sugars and salts, the CELL SAP. Many plant cells in leaves and green stems also have CHLOROPLASTS containing chlorophyll for photosynthesis.

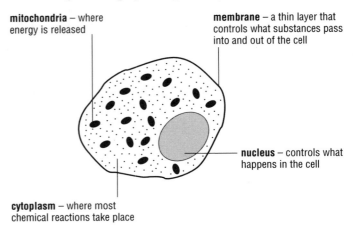

mitochondria – where energy is released

membrane – a thin layer that controls what substances pass into and out of the cell

nucleus – controls what happens in the cell

cytoplasm – where most chemical reactions take place

Figure 1.1.1 A typical animal cell

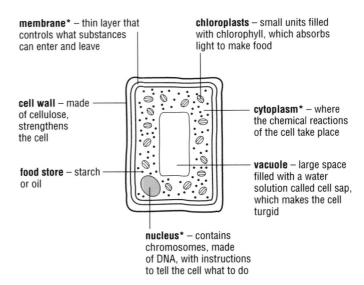

membrane* – thin layer that controls what substances can enter and leave

chloroplasts – small units filled with chlorophyll, which absorbs light to make food

cell wall – made of cellulose, strengthens the cell

cytoplasm* – where the chemical reactions of the cell take place

food store – starch or oil

vacuole – large space filled with a water solution called cell sap, which makes the cell turgid

nucleus* – contains chromosomes, made of DNA, with instructions to tell the cell what to do

Figure 1.1.2 A basic plant cell (parts marked * are common to both plant and animal cells)

Tissues, organs and organ systems

Multicellular organisms show **division of labour**. They are made up of many cells, which show specialisation and which are capable of performing different functions (Figure 1.1.3).

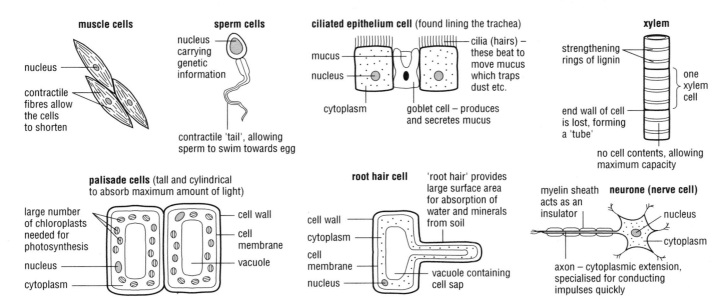

Figure 1.1.3 Different types of cell

A **tissue** is a group of similar cells carrying out the same function (job). Examples include:

- MUSCULAR TISSUE – made up of muscle cells. The cytoplasm is adapted for contraction bringing about movement of the body.
- GLANDULAR TISSUE – the cells produce secretions which are of use to the body, such as saliva, insulin, sebum or mucus.
- XYLEM TISSUE – the cells are adapted for transporting water towards the leaves in plants.
- PHOTOSYNTHETIC TISSUE (in green parts of plants) – consists of palisade cells; these are adapted to absorb the light energy needed for photosynthesis.

An **organ** is a group of different tissues, the function of each tissue contributing to the function of the organ. For example, the function of the stomach is to digest food. In order to do this it must have muscular tissue to churn the food up, glandular tissue to secrete enzymes and nervous tissue.

Organ systems are groups of organs forming a system that has a particular function. All the organs within that system contribute to that function. The digestive system has many organs besides the stomach, including the liver, pancreas, duodenum, ileum and colon.

A very important feature seen in many organs and tissues of animals and plants is a large SURFACE AREA TO VOLUME RATIO. This ensures efficiency of transport of molecules into and out of cells. This is clearly seen in the intestine, where finger-like projections called villi increase the surface area enormously for absorption of food molecules. In the lungs, alveoli increase the surface area to the size of a tennis court for rapid gas exchange. Most plants have leaves which are large and very flat to maximise light absorption. The root

system of a 4-month-old rye grass plant has a surface area measuring 639 m², maximising absorption of water.

In order to bring about this rapid exchange of materials there must also be a thin membrane and a moist surface, both of which are provided by the cell membranes of the organ concerned. Finally there must be a good transport system to take away the products absorbed.

Quick Questions
● ●

1 What are the seven characteristics of all living organisms?
2 Copy and complete Table 1.1.1, indicating which structures are present or absent in each type of cell.

Table 1.1.1

Cell structure	Animal cell	Plant cell
Nucleus		
Chloroplast		
Cytoplasm		
Cell membrane		
Cell wall		
Mitochondria		
Vacuole		

3 Which part of the cell:
   a) Releases energy?
   b) Contains the hereditary information?
   c) Controls movement of substances into and out of the cell?
   d) Is involved in photosynthesis?
4 What is a tissue? Give an example of an animal tissue and a plant tissue.

1.2 Transport across boundaries

Diffusion

Diffusion is the movement of molecules of a liquid or gas from a region of high concentration to a region of low concentration (that is, *down* the concentration gradient) until both concentrations are the same. The greater the difference between the two concentrations, the faster is the rate of diffusion.

Examples include movement of gases between the blood and the air in the alveoli in the lungs (Figure 1.2.1), and movement of gases into and out of leaves through tiny openings called stomata. Other substances such as water, sugar and ions can also move through cell membranes by diffusion. The greater the surface area over which diffusion can take place, the faster will be the rate.

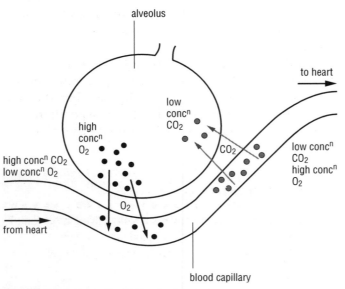

Figure 1.2.1 Diffusion of gases in the lung

Osmosis

Osmosis is a special case of diffusion involving water molecules only. It can only occur across membranes. Osmosis is the movement of water from a weak solution (that is, a high concentration of water) to a strong solution (a low concentration of water) across a **selectively permeable membrane** until both concentrations are the same (Figure 1.2.2).

overall movement of water this way

dilute solution

concentrated solution

this solution becomes *more* concentrated as water moves out

this solution becomes *less* concentrated as water moves in

cell membrane is partially permeable; the holes in it allow only water molecules to pass through

key

· water molecules

⬤ solute particles

Figure 1.2.2 Osmosis

Osmosis can occur in all cells. Animal cells such as red blood cells may either take in or lose water by osmosis, depending on the concentration of the solution surrounding them, and may burst or shrink (Figure 1.2.3).

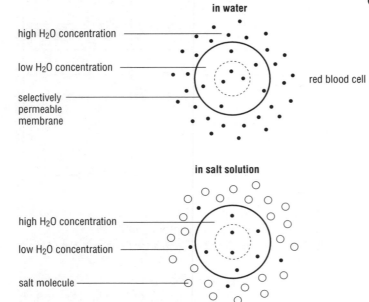

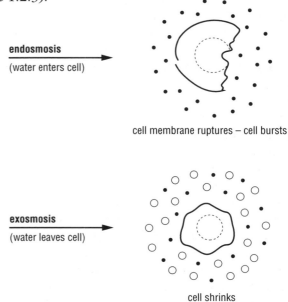

Figure 1.2.3 Water movement in and out of cells by osmosis

This is also true for plant cells. The cell wall is fully permeable and the cell membrane is selectively permeable. If a plant cell is placed in a strong sugar or salt solution it will lose water by osmosis and the cell becomes **plasmolysed** as shown in Figure 1.2.4.

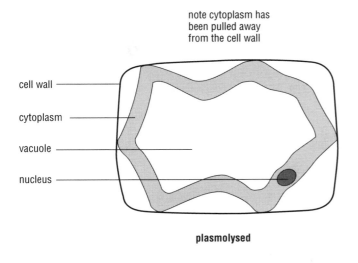

note cytoplasm has been pulled away from the cell wall

cell wall
cytoplasm
vacuole
nucleus

plasmolysed

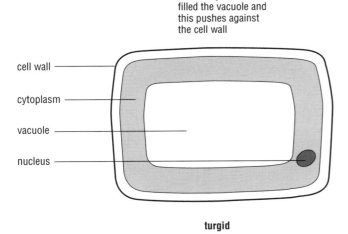

note entry of water has filled the vacuole and this pushes against the cell wall

cell wall
cytoplasm
vacuole
nucleus

turgid

Figure 1.2.4 Turgid and plasmolysed cells

In pure water or a weak solution the cells would take up water. When a plant cell has absorbed as much water as possible it is said to be fully **turgid** (see Figure 1.2.4). The pressure created within the cell supports it (like air in a balloon) and this is how many plant structures such as seedlings gain support.

Root hair cells absorb water from a 'weak' soil solution by osmosis. Roots are usually surrounded by a dilute (weak) solution of mineral salts in which the concentration of water molecules is greater than in the cell sap. Water enters the root by osmosis.

Active transport

Active transport is the reverse of diffusion. Here molecules or ions move *against* the concentration gradient (that is, from a low concentration to a high concentration). It occurs only in living cells and requires energy from aerobic respiration. Therefore the process stops if little or no oxygen is available, or if metabolic poisons like cyanide are used. Active transport occurs in root hair cells, which need to accumulate large quantities of certain minerals. The concentration of mineral ions is higher in the root cells than in the soil water and so they must be pumped against a concentration gradient into the root cells by active transport (Figure 1.2.5). It also occurs in the kidney where substances such as salt, glucose and amino acids are reabsorbed back into the blood from RENAL FLUID (pre-urine). It also occurs in the gut where digested food, such as glucose, is absorbed into the blood.

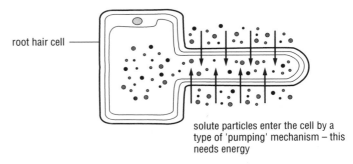

root hair cell

solute particles enter the cell by a type of 'pumping' mechanism – this needs energy

Figure 1.2.5 Active transport: intake of mineral ions against a concentration gradient

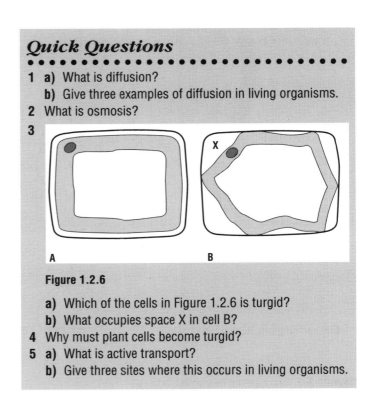

Quick Questions

1 a) What is diffusion?
  b) Give three examples of diffusion in living organisms.
2 What is osmosis?
3

Figure 1.2.6

A   B

  a) Which of the cells in Figure 1.2.6 is turgid?
  b) What occupies space X in cell B?
4 Why must plant cells become turgid?
5 a) What is active transport?
  b) Give three sites where this occurs in living organisms.

1.3 Cell division

Within the nucleus of a cell can be found the **hereditary material**. This is found in the structures called **chromosomes**. In human nuclei there are 46 chromosomes (two sets – the **diploid** condition – each with 23 chromosomes). The chromosomes carry a large number of **genes**. These genes are responsible for determining characteristics. Individuals show variations in these characteristics. This is because there are slight variations in the genes for these characteristics. These variants of genes are known as **alleles**. Before a cell can divide it must make copies of these chromosomes for the daughter cells. Cell division must occur for GROWTH to take place or to REPLACE DAMAGED OR WORN-OUT CELLS. Cell division is also used in reproduction. When cell division is used for growth or ASEXUAL REPRODUCTION, an exact copy of each chromosome is made so that the daughter cells formed are **genetically identical** to the parent cell. This type of cell division is called **mitosis** (Figure 1.3.1).

1 the nucleus of each body cell has 23 pairs of chromosomes, making 46 in total

2 two copies (chromatids) of each chromosome become visible as they thicken and contract

3 chromosome pairs line up in the middle of each cell, with partners in each chromosome pair next to each other

4 chromatids now separate as they are 'pulled' to opposite poles of the cell

5 when a cell divides into two a copy of each chromosome passes into each new cell so both 'daughter cells' contain 46 chromosomes – each cell has identical chromosomes; new nuclear membrane forms

6 the two daughter cells separate

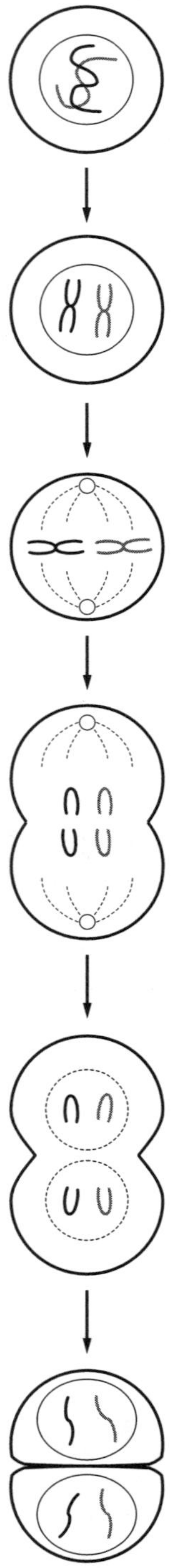

Figure 1.3.1 The stages of mitosis in humans

1 chromosomes become visible in the 'mother' cell

2 the two copies (chromatids) of each chromosome become visible as they thicken and contract

3 each pair of chromosomes lines up in the middle of the cell, with partners in each chromosome pair next to each other

4 fibres pull on the chromosomes, pulling each chromosome of a pair to opposite ends of the cell

5 two cells are formed, although they may not separate completely

6 the chromatids on each chromosome separate, and four new 'daughter' cells are made. The chromatids are now chromosomes. Each cell has half the number of chromosomes of the 'mother' cell

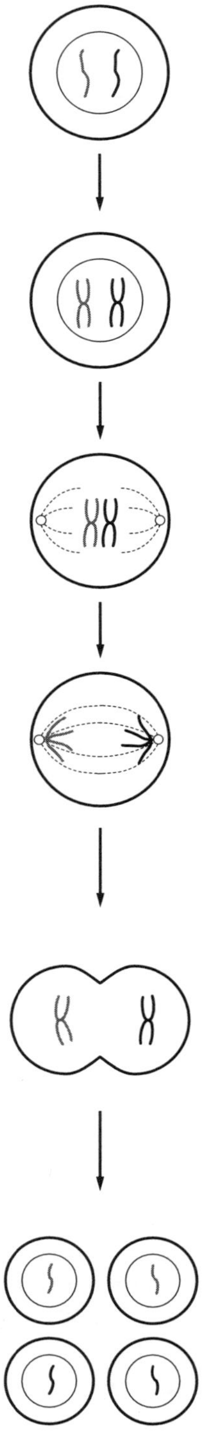

Figure 1.3.2 The stages of meiosis in humans

When cell division is used for sexual reproduction, again copies of the chromosomes are made and then the cell divides twice so that four sex cells (**gametes**) are produced. These gametes contain only half the genetic material, that is, 23 chromosomes in humans or one set (the **haploid** condition). This type of cell division is called **meiosis**, and occurs in the **gonads** (sex organs). It is also known as a **reduction division** because of the halving of the chromosome number (Figure 1.3.2). When the gametes are joined at fertilisation a **zygote** is formed, which will have the normal number of chromosomes, that is 46 in humans (see section 2.7). This cell then divides repeatedly by mitosis to form a new individual (Figure 1.3.3).

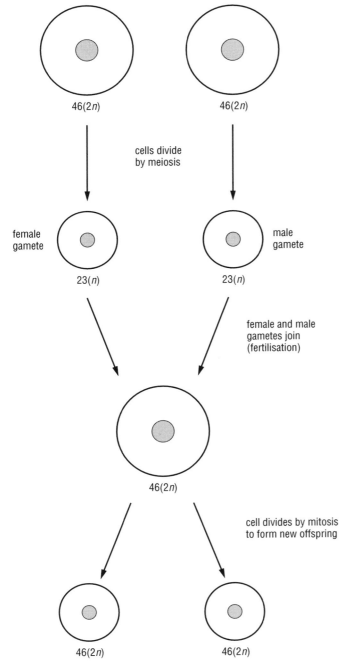

Figure 1.3.3 Sexual reproduction in humans

Quick Questions

1 What structures in the nucleus carry the hereditary information?
2 Name the types of cell division involved in:
  a) producing genetically identical daughter cells;
  b) producing gametes.
3 What type of cell division is involved in asexual reproduction?
4 How many chromosomes are there in:
  a) a normal human cell?
  b) a normal human gamete?
5

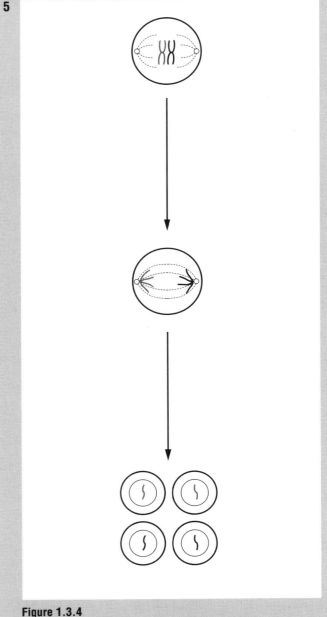

Figure 1.3.4

  a) Name the type of cell division shown in Figure 1.3.4.
  b) What happens to the chromosome number?
  c) Where does this occur in animals?

Section One: Examination Questions

1. (a) All human beings grow. List **five** other features (characteristics) that humans and other animals show. [5]
   (b) What do green plants need which animals do **not** need? [1]

   (WJEC, Foundation, Specimen)

2.

animal cell

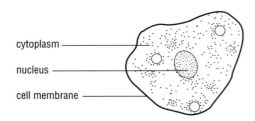

plant cell

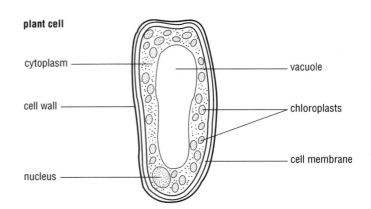

Fill in the table below to show **three** differences between plant and animal cells. Use the drawings above to help you. [3]

	Plant cells	Animal cells
1		
2		
3		

(WJEC, Foundation, Specimen)

3. (a) Plants are made of cells. The diagram below shows a plant cell. Complete the table and give **one** function for each part. [6]

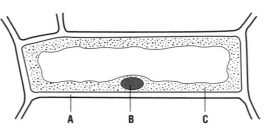

	Name	Function
A		
B		
C		

(b) Animals are made of cells. Describe **two** similarities and **two** differences between plant and animal cells. [4]

(SEG Double Award, Foundation, Specimen)

4. The diagram below shows a sperm.

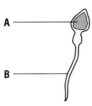

(a) Name the part labelled **A** [on the line provided]. [1]
(b) Part **A** contains information which is passed from the father to his child.
  (i) Which structures in part **A** contain this information? [1]
  (ii) What use is this information to the cells of a growing baby? [1]
(c) How does the part labelled **B** help the sperm to carry out its function? [1]
(d) The diagram below shows a cell from the root of a plant.

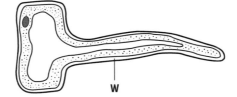

  (i) Complete the passage below.

  Structure **W** is made of .... The process which helps this cell to absorb mineral ions from the soil is called .... [2]
  (ii) The root of a plant has many cells like the one shown in the diagram. How do the large numbers and the shape of these cells help a plant to obtain enough water from the soil? [1]

(London Double Award, Foundation, Specimen)

5. In an osmosis experiment, 10 cylinders of potato each **exactly** 50 mm long were used.

Five of the cylinders were placed in water.
Five of the cylinders were placed in 25% sugar solution.

After one hour the cylinders were removed from the solution and their surfaces were dried. They were placed on the graph paper as shown in the diagram below.

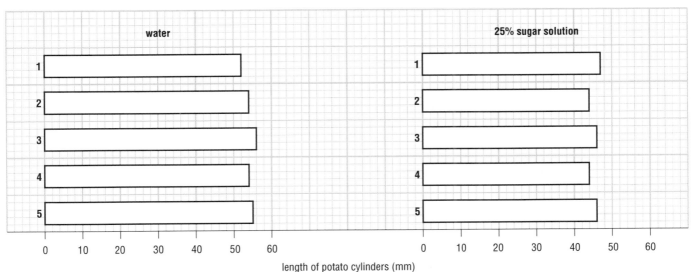

(a) Calculate the average length of the cylinders that were in water. [1]
(b) The cylinders that were in water and those which were in sugar solution had different average lengths. Explain how this happened. [3]
(c) Which other measurements could have been taken to show that the cylinders had changed during the experiment? [2]

(London Double Award, Higher, Specimen)

6. This question is about cell division. Complete the table below by putting a tick in the correct column or columns. The first answer is done for you.

Feature	Type of cell division	
	Meiosis	Mitosis
Changes take place in the nucleus	✓	✓
Produces gametes		
Produces daughter cells with identical chromosomes		
Half the chromosomes are passed to each daughter cell		
Homologous chromosomes are randomly assorted into the daughter cells		
Mutations can occur to change the genetic code		
Chromatids are separated by fibres within the cell		

(SEG, Higher, Specimen)

7. The drawings below represent seven stages of mitosis.

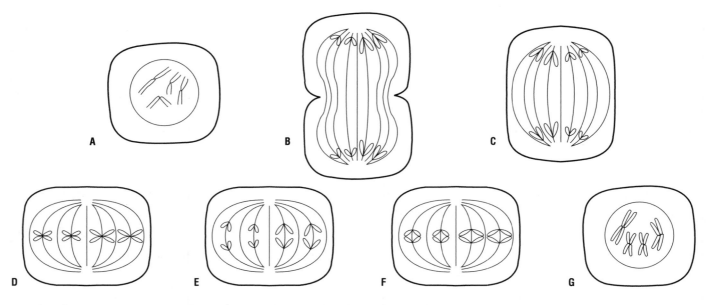

The drawings are **not** in the correct order of what happens to the chromosomes during mitosis. Rearrange them so that they are in the correct order.

The parent cell with four chromsomes is shown in drawing **A**.   [2]

(SEG, Higher, 1994)

8. (a) Choose words from this list to complete the sentences that follow. Each word may be used once or not at all.

cells	organs
chloroplasts	organisms
chromosomes	nucleus
genes	tissues

Each body cell contains a .... which controls the cell's activities and characteristics. This contains pairs of ...., which are made up of a number of small units of inheritance called ....
Collections of similar cells working together are called .... These make up ....
which work together as systems allowing .... to survive.   [6]
(b) Cells are surrounded by a cell membrane. Give **two** jobs carried out by a cell membrane.   [2]

(SEG Double Award, Foundation, Specimen)

Section
TWO

Humans as organisms

2.1 Nutrition and digestion

In order to remain healthy a human diet must have balanced proportions of the following:

- Carbohydrates.
- Proteins.
- Lipids (fats).
- Minerals.
- Vitamins.
- Water.
- Roughage (fibre).

Carbohydrates are found in food such as potatoes, bread, cereals, pasta, rice, cakes, biscuits, fruits and chocolate. They provide us with energy when it is required rapidly. Examples of carbohydrates include glucose, sucrose, maltose, lactose, glycogen (found in liver and muscle), starch and cellulose (found in plant cell walls).

Lipids (or fats) are found in egg yolk, milk, cheese, butter, margarine and fatty meat. They are also needed to provide energy and in the formation of cell membranes. They are also used to insulate some animals, like whales and penguins, against extremely cold conditions. Animal fat contains a high proportion of saturated fat and cholesterol, this may cause problems. If cholesterol is deposited in arteries it causes thickening of the walls, which can lead to high blood pressure and other circulatory disorders, including blood clots and increased risk of heart attack and strokes.

Both carbohydrate and fat are energy-rich foods. The more active people are, the more of these they need to provide energy. The amount of energy needed and therefore the carbohydrate and fat intake will also vary according to age, sex and state of health.

If people eat more energy-rich food than they can use, the surplus is stored as fat. If this continues for some time the person will become obese. This causes stress on the heart and skeleton and makes movement difficult. A lack of carbohydrate and fat will lead to a lack of energy and, in children, slow growth.

Proteins are present in all meats, and also in fish, egg white, cheese, milk and pulses like beans and peas. They are used for growth and repair of parts of cells such as cell membranes (see page 2). If there is too little protein in the diet, growth becomes stunted. In some countries lack of protein is a major cause of malnutrition and can give rise to a disease known as **kwashiorkor**. Enzymes, which are involved in most chemical reactions in the body, are made of protein.

Proteins, carbohydrates and lipids are needed in relatively large quantities compared to the following nutrients.

Minerals, are needed in much smaller amounts. These are inorganic elements and a wide variety is needed by the body, including:

- Iron, needed to make haemoglobin in red blood cells. Lack of this, and therefore fewer red blood cells, leads to ANAEMIA, which makes a person weak and tired. This is because their blood cannot carry enough oxygen for respiration around the body, which leads to a lack of energy. Iron is found especially in red meat and in green vegetables such as spinach and watercress.
- Calcium, needed by growing bones and teeth, and also by muscles for contraction. A lack of calcium causes RICKETS in which the leg bones cannot support the weight of the body and therefore bend. Rich sources of calcium are milk, cheese and most vegetables.

Vitamins form a group of organic substances required in small quantities for normal health. They include:

- Vitamin C, needed for healthy cells, especially those that cover and line our bodies, particularly the skin and blood vessels. Shortage of vitamin C can lead to SCURVY. Here the gums start to bleed and wounds do not heal properly. Vegetables and fruit, especially citrus fruits, are rich in vitamin C.
- Vitamin D, which helps the body to absorb calcium from the food in the intestine. Therefore a lack of it causes rickets. Vitamin D is made in the skin by the action of UV light. It is found in fish liver oils, such as cod liver oil, and in milk and egg yolk.

A shortage of vitamins and minerals can lead to various types of diseases which are called deficiency diseases.

The main component of cytoplasm is water. Water has several other functions in the body:

- Transport of materials, for example in the xylem in plants and in the plasma of animals.
- Cooling the body, for example sweating in humans and transpiration in plants.
- Transfer of gametes (sperm).
- A raw material in chemical reactions such as photosynthesis.

Roughage or fibre is needed to stimulate the movement of material along the intestine. Lack of this can lead to CONSTIPATION, PILES and other bowel disorders like CANCER.

Simple tests for some food substances are shown in Table 2.1.1 opposite.

Table 2.1.1 Summary of tests used for detection of food substances

Substance	Reagent	Method	Positive result
Glucose	Benedict's	Equal volumes of reagent and suspension of sample heated together in water-bath	Pale blue Benedict's produces a brick red precipitate
Starch	Iodine solution	Drops of iodine solution added to sample	Blue/black colour
Protein	Sodium hydroxide and copper sulphate	Equal volumes of sodium hydroxide solution and suspension of sample, drops of copper sulphate added	Lilac colour on shaking
Fat	Ethanol/propan-2-ol	Shake sample with alcohol, pour off top layer into water	White cloudy emulsion is formed
Vitamin C	DCPIP solution	Add drops of sample to DCPIP	Dark blue of DCPIP turns colourless

Digestion

The main function of the digestive system is to change large, complex, insoluble molecules into small, simple, diffusible ones.

Digestion is both MECHANICAL and CHEMICAL. Mechanical digestion is brought about in the mouth by the action of the teeth (chewing or mastication). Food is mechanically broken up into smaller pieces, increasing the surface area.

Teeth

These are used to bite off and chew food in order to produce smaller pieces, which are easier to swallow and to digest chemically.

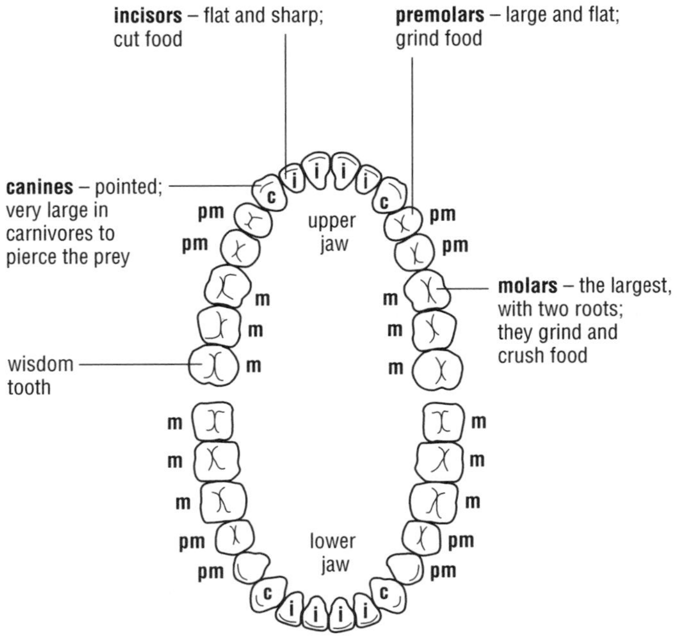

There are four types of teeth (Figure 2.1.1) each with a different shape related to its function:

- INCISORS are shaped like chisels and are used for cutting food.
- CANINES are pointed and are used for holding and piercing the food.
- PREMOLARS have two blunted points or cusps and are used for crushing and grinding food.
- MOLARS have a similar shape to premolars but are larger and have four or more cusps; they too are used for crushing and grinding.

Teeth have a highly organised structure, as shown in Figure 2.1.2.

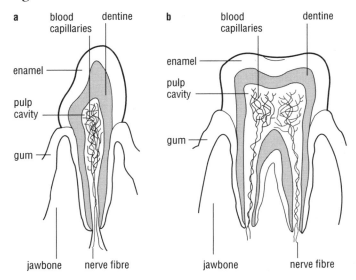

Figure 2.1.2 Section through (**a**) an incisor tooth (at the front of the mouth), (**b**) a molar tooth (at the back of the mouth)

incisors – flat and sharp; cut food

premolars – large and flat; grind food

canines – pointed; very large in carnivores to pierce the prey

molars – the largest, with two roots; they grind and crush food

wisdom tooth

upper jaw

lower jaw

Figure 2.1.1 The arrangement of teeth in the upper and lower jaw of an adult

Mechanical digestion continues as food is moved through the alimentary canal by muscular contraction of the gut wall. This process is called **peristalsis**. In the stomach food is churned to encourage thorough mixing of food and enzymes.

Enzymes

Chemical digestion is carried out by the action of **enzymes**. These are BIOLOGICAL CATALYSTS made by living cells. They can speed up reactions inside cells (intracellular) or outside cells (extracellular). They are often called the body's most important proteins and the way they work depends on their 3D shape (Figure 2.1.3). The part of the enzyme molecule which is involved in enzyme activity is called the **active site**. It is here that specific SUBSTRATES bind to the enzyme.

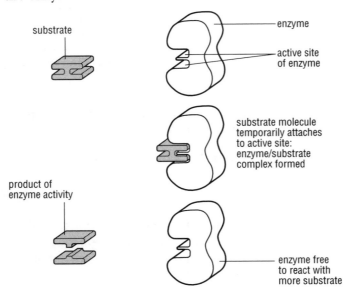

Figure 2.1.3 The 'lock and key' hypothesis of enzyme action

Characteristics of enzymes

- Since they are released at the end of every reaction and not used up they are only needed in small quantities. The same enzyme molecule can process large quantities of **substrate**.
- Temperature influences the rate of enzyme activity. Usually a 10 °C rise doubles the rate of enzyme activity. This is only true up to an OPTIMUM temperature, however. Beyond this point (usually 40 °C) the 3D shape of the active site becomes distorted and the enzyme becomes inactive. The enzyme is said to be **denatured** (Figure 2.1.4). Cooling or even freezing does not destroy enzymes, though it slows down their activity.

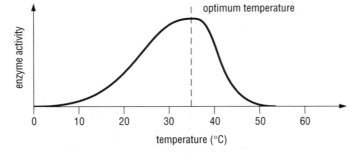

Figure 2.1.4 How enzyme activity varies with temperature

- Enzymes have an OPTIMUM pH at which they are most active. For most enzymes this is around 7 but some work better at extreme pHs; pepsin, for instance, works best at pH 2.
- They are specific; their substrate must fit into the active site in order for the reaction to take place. In most cases enzymes have a single substrate or are active with only a few very similar substrates. Enzymes are frequently named according to their substrates; lipases work on lipids, for example.
- Enzyme activity can be slowed or even completely stopped by inhibitors. These are poisons, and include heavy metals like lead and mercury. They work by combining with the active site of the enzyme.

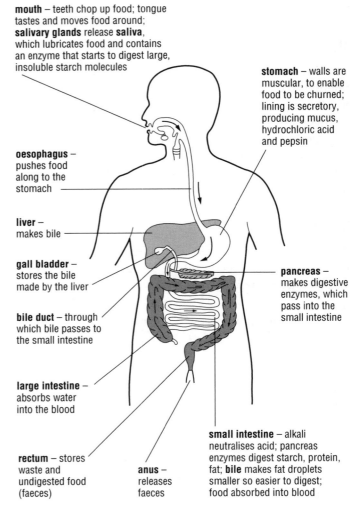

mouth – teeth chop up food; tongue tastes and moves food around; **salivary glands** release **saliva**, which lubricates food and contains an enzyme that starts to digest large, insoluble starch molecules

oesophagus – pushes food along to the stomach

stomach – walls are muscular, to enable food to be churned; lining is secretory, producing mucus, hydrochloric acid and pepsin

liver – makes bile

gall bladder – stores the bile made by the liver

bile duct – through which bile passes to the small intestine

pancreas – makes digestive enzymes, which pass into the small intestine

large intestine – absorbs water into the blood

rectum – stores waste and undigested food (faeces)

anus – releases faeces

small intestine – alkali neutralises acid; pancreas enzymes digest starch, protein, fat; **bile** makes fat droplets smaller so easier to digest; food absorbed into blood

Figure 2.1.5 The human digestive system

Starch, proteins and lipids are insoluble. They are broken down into soluble substances which can be absorbed across the gut lining into the blood stream. The indigestible food which remains makes up the bulk of the faeces, together with bacteria and cells lost from the intestinal lining. The faeces are stored in the rectum until they are discharged through the anus.

Table 2.1.2 Summary of digestion

Region	Enzyme	pH	Substrate	Product
Mouth	Salivary amylase	7	Starch	Maltose
Stomach	Pepsin	2 (hydrochloric acid secreted)	Protein	Polypeptides
	Rennin		Milk	Solidified milk
Small intestine	Pancreatic and small intestinal carbohydrases	8/9	Carbohydrate	Simple sugars
	Proteases		Polypeptide	Amino acids
	Lipase		Lipids	Fatty acids and glycerol
Colon	No enzymes secreted here; the main function is to absorb water from the faeces; infection leads to diarrhoea			

Bile

The liver produces bile from dead, broken-down red blood cells. Bile also contains excess cholesterol. It is stored in the gall bladder, and enters the first part of the small intestine by the bile duct. Bile has two main functions:

- It neutralises the acid from the stomach, so it provides the optimum alkaline pH for the enzymes found in the small intestine.
- It **emulsifies** fat (another example of physical digestion). Here the fat is broken up into tiny droplets and so has a larger surface area for lipases to digest it. This speeds up lipid digestion. Bile is not an enzyme.

Absorption

The final products of digestion are glucose, amino acids, fatty acids and glycerol. There are also tiny fat droplets, minerals and vitamins. **Absorption** of these takes place in the small intestine (ileum) and is made easier by having:

- A huge SURFACE AREA provided by finger-like projections called VILLI (Figure 2.1.6).
- A well-developed BLOOD SUPPLY to take away digested food products and thus maintain concentration gradients.
- A SINGLE LAYER of cells between the blood system and digested food.
- A MOIST LINING across which materials are absorbed.

Most of the products of digestion, including the water-soluble vitamins, are absorbed into the blood capillaries of the villi by diffusion. Active transport may, however, be needed when most of the food molecules have been absorbed and for the absorption of minerals. Fatty acids may recombine with glycerol and are absorbed whole into the lymph of the lacteal vessel and then carried in a fluid called lymph through the lymphatic system. Fat-soluble vitamins are absorbed with these fat droplets.

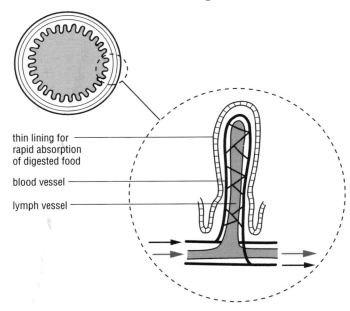

thin lining for rapid absorption of digested food

blood vessel

lymph vessel

Figure 2.1.6 Villi: these increase the surface area through which the products of digestion are absorbed into the blood; their walls are very thin, so the molecules of the digested food are absorbed easily

Quick Questions

1 Why is digestion needed?
2 What are enzymes?
3 What effect do high temperatures have on enzymes?
4 Why are enzymes substrate-specific?
5 In which parts of the digestive system is
   a) Protein digested;
   b) Starch digested?
6 Name the final products of digestion.
7 Where does absorption take place? Name the two processes involved in absorption.

2.2 Circulation

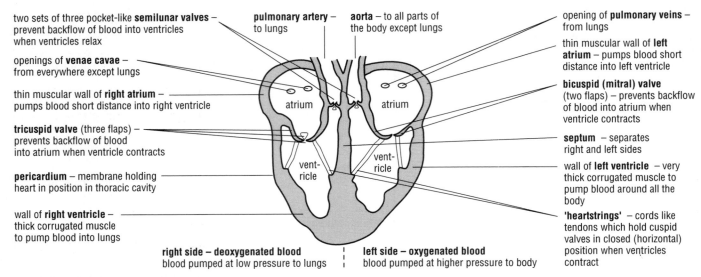

two sets of three pocket-like **semilunar valves** – prevent backflow of blood into ventricles when ventricles relax

openings of **venae cavae** – from everywhere except lungs

thin muscular wall of **right atrium** – pumps blood short distance into right ventricle

tricuspid valve (three flaps) – prevents backflow of blood into atrium when ventricle contracts

pericardium – membrane holding heart in position in thoracic cavity

wall of **right ventricle** – thick corrugated muscle to pump blood into lungs

pulmonary artery – to lungs

aorta – to all parts of the body except lungs

atrium

atrium

vent-ricle

vent-ricle

opening of **pulmonary veins** – from lungs

thin muscular wall of **left atrium** – pumps blood short distance into left ventricle

bicuspid (mitral) valve (two flaps) – prevents backflow of blood into atrium when ventricle contracts

septum – separates right and left sides

wall of **left ventricle** – very thick corrugated muscle to pump blood around all the body

'heartstrings' – cords like tendons which hold cuspid valves in closed (horizontal) position when ventricles contract

right side – deoxygenated blood
blood pumped at low pressure to lungs

left side – oxygenated blood
blood pumped at higher pressure to body

Figure 2.2.1 Longitudinal section through the heart of a mammal

The main function of the circulatory system is in transport of materials around the body. It is also important in the defence of the body. The circulatory system is composed of the heart and blood vessels. The heart is a hollow muscular pump found in the thoracic (chest) cavity (Figure 2.2.1). The function of the heart is to force blood out along the arteries to all organs of the body.

Double circulation

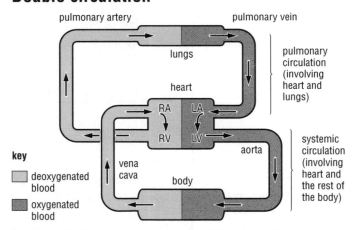

Figure 2.2.2 The double circulation, so called because there are two different circulatory systems joined at the heart. A red blood cell leaving the leg passes through the heart twice in order to return to the leg. The system is closed, which means that blood is enclosed in a series of blood vessels

Passage of blood through the heart

- Blood returns to the atria (auricles) in the vena cava and pulmonary vein.
- Blood fills the atria and they contract.
- Blood pressure in the atria forces open the tricuspid and bicuspid valves.
- Blood flows into the ventricles.
- Ventricles fill with blood and they begin to contract.
- As pressure rises in the contracting ventricles, the tricuspid and bicuspid valves are forced closed.
- The semilunar valves are forced open by increasing blood pressure in the ventricles.
- Blood flows out through the aorta and pulmonary artery.
- The ventricles relax, blood pressure falls and the semilunar valves close.

Arteries, veins and capillaries

Table 2.2.1 Differences between arteries and veins

Arteries	Veins
Carry blood away from the heart	Carry blood towards the heart
Carry oxygenated blood (except the pulmonary artery)	Carry deoxygenated blood (except the pulmonary vein)
Rapid flow under pressure	Slower flow under lower pressure
Blood flows in pulses	Flow is smooth
Thick walls with more elastic and muscular tissue to withstand the higher pressure	Thinner walls with less elastic and muscular tissue
Valves absent	Valves present to ensure unidirectional flow of blood towards the heart
Small round lumen	Large oval-shaped lumen to reduce resistance to flow

Within the organs of the body blood flows through an extensive network of capillaries, which ensures that most of the cells are close to a blood supply. The walls are extremely thin and a fluid called **tissue fluid** is forced out between the cells. It is very similar to **plasma** (see below) except that it has no cells. It contains dissolved materials, such as oxygen and glucose, needed by the body. Substances produced by the cells, such as carbon dioxide and hormones, pass back in to the blood. Some tissue fluid is absorbed by the lymphatic system and here the fluid is called **lymph**.

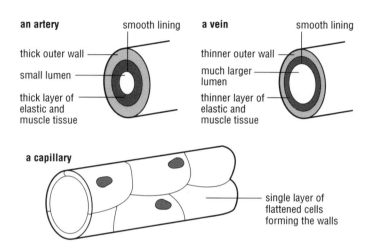

Figure 2.2.3 Blood vessels (not to scale)

Blood

This has two parts: plasma and cells.

1 Plasma – transports many important materials around the body, including:

- Carbon dioxide from all body cells to the lungs.
- Soluble products of digestion from the intestine to other parts of the body.
- Urea from the liver to the kidneys.
- Hormones from glands to other organs or cells of the body.
- Heat from areas of high metabolic activity (such as muscle during exercise) to other regions where the heat may be lost (such as the skin).
- Antibodies used in defence of the body against foreign antigens.
- Vitamins and minerals.

2 Cells – there are two types: red blood cells and white cells (Figure 2.2.4).

Red blood cells or erythrocytes have a biconcave shape that gives them a larger surface area : volume ratio. This allows them to absorb oxygen more quickly. They have no nucleus. This gives the cell more 'space' for more haemoglobin and therefore more oxygen can be carried.

Red blood cells are made in the bone marrow and live for approximately 120 days. They are destroyed in the liver and are used to make bile pigments.

In the lungs, where there is a high oxygen concentration, they rapidly pick up oxygen to form oxyhaemoglobin. In other organs where there is a lower oxygen concentration the oxyhaemoglobin quickly dissociates (splits up) into haemoglobin and oxygen. The oxygen released is used by the cells.

White cells have nuclei, and form part of the body's defence system. There are two main types known as:

- Lymphocytes (agranulocytes). These produce antibodies and antitoxins which destroy foreign antigens (see section 2.10).
- Phagocytes (granulocytes or polymorphs). These ingest foreign microbes or damaged cells within the body (see Figure 2.9.2, page 37).

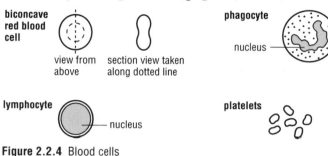

Figure 2.2.4 Blood cells

Blood also contains PLATELETS. These are small fragments of cells and therefore have no nucleus. Clotting occurs when platelets are activated by exposure to air or damaged cells. They release an enzyme called THROMBOPLASTIN which, via several steps, causes the production of FIBRIN from soluble FIBRINOGEN. Fibrin forms a meshwork in which blood cells become entangled, forming a scab.

Quick Questions

1 Name
   a) The liquid part of the blood;
   b) The cells found in the blood.
2 List five things transported in the circulating blood.
3 What is the function of platelets?
4 How is oxygen transported?
5 Name the four chambers of the heart.
6 Name the valves of the heart, where they are found and their function.
7 Movement of blood by the heart depends on two important changes within the heart. What are these?
8 List four differences between arteries and veins.
9 How are capillaries adapted for their function?
10 Name
   a) The veins that deliver blood to the heart;
   b) The arteries that carry blood away from the heart.

2.3 Breathing and respiration

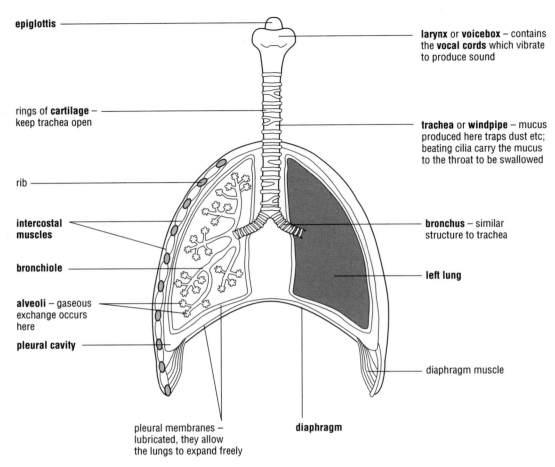

epiglottis

larynx or voicebox – contains the vocal cords which vibrate to produce sound

rings of cartilage – keep trachea open

trachea or windpipe – mucus produced here traps dust etc; beating cilia carry the mucus to the throat to be swallowed

rib

intercostal muscles

bronchus – similar structure to trachea

bronchiole

left lung

alveoli – gaseous exchange occurs here

pleural cavity

diaphragm muscle

pleural membranes – lubricated, they allow the lungs to expand freely

diaphragm

Figure 2.3.1 The breathing system

Breathing refers to the process of getting oxygen into the body and getting rid of carbon dioxide from the body. The breathing system is found in the chest or thoracic cavity. It is protected by the rib-cage. The diaphragm forms the floor of the thoracic cavity. It is composed of a tough sheet of tissue and muscle. The intercostal muscles and the muscles of the diaphragm bring about breathing movements.

Figure 2.3.1 shows the main structures in the system and some of their functions.

Breathing involves movement of air into and out of the lungs brought about by changes in air pressure within the system. To inhale:

- Intercostal muscles contract, moving the ribs upwards and outwards.
- Diaphragm muscle contracts and the diaphragm flattens.

Both these movements increase the volume within the thorax and decrease air pressure within the lungs below that of the atmosphere outside. As a result air is forced into the lungs.

Breathing out is the reverse of this process: muscles relax, volume decreases, pressure increases and air is forced out of the lungs.

Gaseous exchange

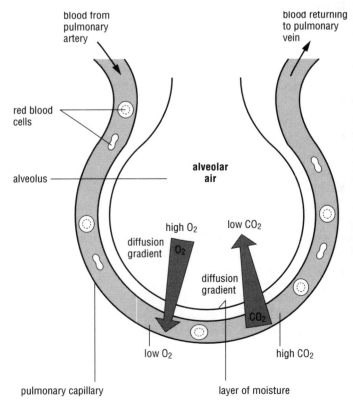

blood from pulmonary artery

blood returning to pulmonary vein

red blood cells

alveolar air

alveolus

high O$_2$

low CO$_2$

diffusion gradient O$_2$

diffusion gradient

CO$_2$

low O$_2$

high CO$_2$

pulmonary capillary

layer of moisture

Figure 2.3.2 Gaseous exchange in the lungs

The lungs have all the features that make them efficient structures for gaseous exchange:

- Large surface area (alveoli).
- Thin surface across which gases diffuse.
- Moist surface.
- Transport system to maintain a CONCENTRATION GRADIENT for gases to diffuse.

In gaseous exchange both carbon dioxide and oxygen move across the alveolar surface. In other organisms this process may take place at other surfaces, such as gills in fish and mesophyll cells in leaves.

The exchange of gases occurs along their concentration gradients by diffusion. Oxygen moves from a high concentration in the alveolar air to a low concentration in the blood. Carbon dioxide moves in the opposite direction from a high concentration in the blood to a lower concentration in the alveolar air. Both gases dissolve in the thin layer of moisture lining the alveolus.

Remember that the diffusion gradient must be constantly maintained. This is achieved by:

- A constant flow of blood through the capillaries.
- Changing the alveolar air by breathing (ventilation).

Respiration

Respiration is the process in which energy is released within living cells. This energy may be used for:

- Mechanical work such as muscle contraction, or swimming of sperm.
- Chemical synthesis, that is, to build up larger molecules using smaller ones. Examples include building new protein in muscle cells from amino acids, new cell walls in plant cells from glucose, and making more enzymes from amino acids.
- Producing body heat to maintain constant body temperature in mammals and birds.
- Transport of materials across boundaries by active transport.

Normally this energy is released/transferred from food molecules, such as glucose, using oxygen as shown below:

$$\text{oxygen} + \text{glucose} \longrightarrow \text{carbon dioxide} + \text{water} + \text{ENERGY}$$

$$6O_2 + C_6H_{12}O_6 \xrightarrow{\text{enzymes}} 6CO_2 + 6H_2O + \text{ENERGY}$$

This is called AEROBIC respiration as it involves the use of oxygen. The energy is stored in the form of a chemical known simply as ATP and this reaction takes place in cell organelles called **mitochondria**. ATP can be thought of as the energy currency of the body. More mitochondria occur in cells where more energy is needed, such as muscle cells.

Anaerobic respiration

ANAEROBIC RESPIRATION occurs when oxygen is in short supply or when no oxygen is available. It takes place in the cytoplasm and here the glucose is not completely broken down and much less energy (ATP) is produced. In muscle cells this leads to the production of **lactic acid**:

$$\text{glucose} \rightarrow \text{lactic acid} + \text{energy}$$

In muscle cells that are contracting vigorously and not receiving enough oxygen this lactic acid can lead to fatigue and cramp. Far less energy is released because the breakdown of glucose is incomplete. The lactic acid must be got rid of because it is poisonous (toxic), and to do this more oxygen has to be taken into the body; this is why rapid breathing/panting continues after exercise. This extra oxygen is sometimes known as the **oxygen debt**. The lactic acid is converted back to glycogen in the liver or muscle. It may also be converted to carbon dioxide and water.

Anaerobic respiration takes place in microorganisms such as yeast. Here alcohol and carbon dioxide are produced and the process is sometimes called fermentation:

$$\text{glucose} \rightarrow \text{alcohol} + \text{carbon dioxide} + \text{energy}$$

This process is made use of in the baking and brewing industries (see section 7.2).

Quick Questions
● ●

1 What is the function of the cilia and mucus found in the trachea and bronchi?
2 Which blood vessel
   a) Brings blood to the lungs?
   b) Takes blood away from the lungs?
3 What is the function of the pleural membranes?
4 What is gaseous exchange?
5 Explain why oxygen diffuses from the alveoli into the blood while carbon dioxide follows the reverse route.
6 How are the alveoli adapted for gaseous exchange?
7 Explain why air is drawn into the lungs when we inspire.
8 What is
   a) The word equation for aerobic respiration?
   b) The chemical equation for aerobic respiration?
9 Where in the cell does aerobic respiration take place?
10 What is the name of the energy currency of the body?
11 Give three ways in which anaerobic respiration differs from aerobic respiration.
12 Where does anaerobic respiration take place in cells?
13 What are the products of anaerobic respiration in yeast?
14 Under what circumstances does anaerobic respiration take place in muscles?
15 What is the word equation for anaerobic respiration in muscle?
16 What is the oxygen debt?

2.4 Nervous system

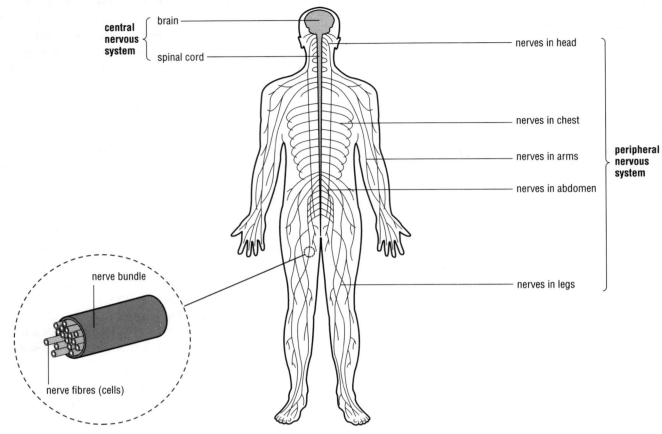

Figure 2.4.1 The nervous system, and a section across a nerve bundle

In animals coordination is achieved through the NERVOUS SYSTEM and the ENDOCRINE SYSTEM. Both these systems allow humans to respond to external stimuli and coordinate their behaviour.

The nervous system (Figure 2.4.1) has two parts:

- The CENTRAL NERVOUS SYSTEM (CNS) made up of the brain and spinal cord.

- The PERIPHERAL NERVOUS SYSTEM made up of sense organs, nerves and their nerve fibres found outside the CNS.

The basic unit of the nervous system is the nerve cell or NEURONE, of which there are three basic types: the MOTOR neurone, the SENSORY neurone and the RELAY (INTERMEDIATE) neurone.

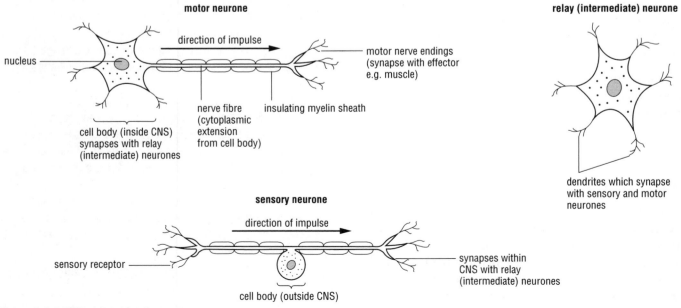

Figure 2.4.2 Different types of neurone

Neurones of all types transmit information in the form of IMPULSES – waves of ELECTRICAL ACTIVITY that pass down the length of a nerve fibre. These impulses, once started, will continue along the length of the fibre unimpeded and at the same speed until they reach the end of the fibre.

Where two neurones meet, the junction between them is called a **synapse**. These occur between sensory and relay neurones and between relay and motor neurones inside the CNS. Here the impulse changes from an electrical nature to a chemical one and the speed is temporarily slowed down. As an impulse arrives at a synapse a NEUROTRANSMITTER substance is released. This diffuses across the synaptic gap (Figure 2.4.3). It causes an impulse to be sent along the next neurone. Many painkillers and certain types of drugs work by interfering with the transmission of the impulse at the synapse.

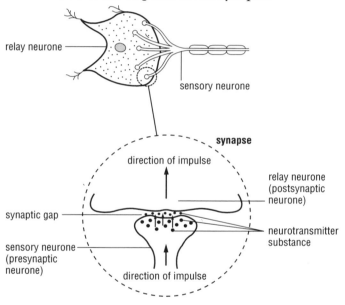

Figure 2.4.3 How an impulse crosses a synapse

Actions performed with help of the nervous system

Automatic actions, like breathing and heartbeat, are not under our conscious control and they are not caused by an external stimulus.

Voluntary actions are controlled by the will, for example, we decide whether we want to raise an arm or leg. These actions are controlled by the CEREBRAL HEMISPHERES of the brain.

Reflex actions, like blinking, are always the result of some external stimulus and the result is always an involuntary one. The nature of the response to a definite stimulus is always the same. Some reflex actions are under the control of the brain and are known as cranial reflexes. The change in pupil size, sometimes known as the iris reflex, is an example of a cranial reflex.

Other reflex actions are under the control of the spinal cord and are known as spinal reflexes. An example of a spinal reflex is the knee jerk reflex. The brain and spinal cord act as coordinators/analysers.

Reflex actions involve all three types of neurone. In a reflex action:

- The STIMULUS is received by a RECEPTOR, in some cases a SENSE ORGAN such as the eye.
- SENSORY impulses are passed from the receptor along sensory neurones towards the CNS.
- The impulses reach either the BRAIN or SPINAL CORD which coordinates a response.
- The brain or spinal cord then sends MOTOR impulses out along motor neurones.
- These impulses reach either MUSCLES or GLANDS which bring about a RESPONSE to the stimulus. These organs are called EFFECTOR ORGANS.

The path the nerve impulses follow is called a REFLEX ARC.

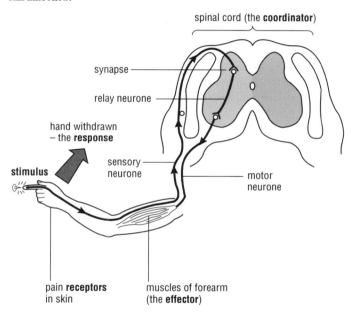

Figure 2.4.4 An example of a reflex arc

Mammalian sensory receptors

The ability to respond to a stimulus depends on the presence of receptors. When stimulated, these send electrical impulses along sensory neurones to the brain or spinal cord. There are various types of stimuli:

- Mechanical (such as pressure and pain).
- Temperature.
- Sound.
- Light.
- Chemical.

Receptors may be evenly distributed or concentrated in one area. Sometimes they may be organised to form a special organ such as the eye and ear.

Receptors in the skin

There are different types of receptors found here:

- Mechanical receptors, responding either to light contact or to increasing pressure which may result in the sensation of touch or pain.
- Temperature receptors, which are sensitive to changes/differences in temperature. They indicate whether we are gaining or losing heat.

Chemical receptors

These give us the senses of smell and taste. Very little is known about the sense of smell, other than the receptor cells are stimulated directly by the molecules of the substance that they come into contact with. The receptors are found on the tongue and the lining of the nose.

Sound receptors

These are found in the ear and are sensitive to sound (vibrations of the air). They allow us to hear. The ear also has receptors that enable us to keep our balance because they are sensitive to changes in the position of the body.

Light receptors

In most vertebrates these are usually grouped together to form a sense organ, the eye.

The eye

The structure of this organ is shown in Figure 2.4.5.

The retina

The retina contains the light-sensitive cells known as the rods and cones. Cones respond to light of high intensity, whereas rods respond to light of low intensity. Cones allow us to see in colour and produce very detailed, well-defined images. Rods produce less well-defined images in black and white. The cones are concentrated in the yellow spot or fovea found directly opposite the centre of the lens. This is the region of greatest sensitivity. The rods are found in decreasing concentrations the further they are from the fovea.

Image formation

Light enters the eye through the CORNEA. The rays of light must be brought to focus on the retina. Light is focused by the cornea and the LENS on to the retina. Note that the image on the retina is inverted and smaller than the object. Sensory impulses are then sent via the OPTIC NERVE to the brain (Figure 2.4.6). The brain interprets these impulses and we 'see' the object in its upright position and its correct size.

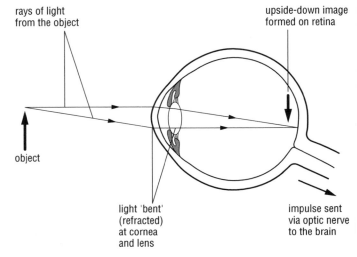

rays of light from the object

upside-down image formed on retina

object

light 'bent' (refracted) at cornea and lens

impulse sent via optic nerve to the brain

Figure 2.4.6 Image formation in the eye

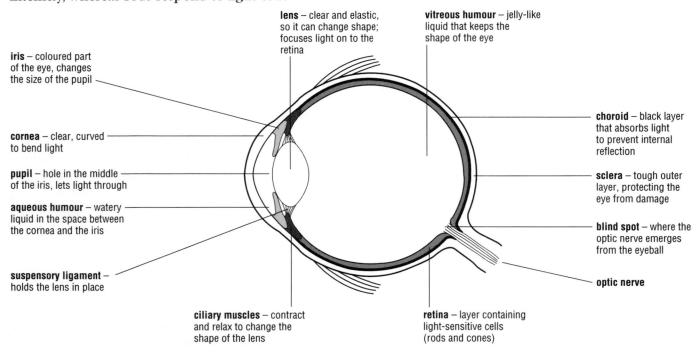

lens – clear and elastic, so it can change shape; focuses light on to the retina

vitreous humour – jelly-like liquid that keeps the shape of the eye

iris – coloured part of the eye, changes the size of the pupil

cornea – clear, curved to bend light

pupil – hole in the middle of the iris, lets light through

aqueous humour – watery liquid in the space between the cornea and the iris

suspensory ligament – holds the lens in place

choroid – black layer that absorbs light to prevent internal reflection

sclera – tough outer layer, protecting the eye from damage

blind spot – where the optic nerve emerges from the eyeball

optic nerve

ciliary muscles – contract and relax to change the shape of the lens

retina – layer containing light-sensitive cells (rods and cones)

Figure 2.4.5 Inside the human eye (horizontal section)

Accommodation (focusing)

The shape of the lens may be changed by altering the tension in the SUSPENSORY LIGAMENTS. This allows us to focus on near and distant objects. The nearer the object the more the light from it must be bent (refracted) and the more rounded the lens must be.

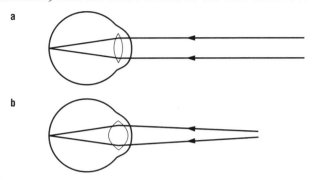

Figure 2.4.7 How the eye focuses: **(a)** for distant objects, the ciliary muscles relax, the tension in the suspensory ligaments increases, pulling the lens into a thinner shape, converging the light less; **(b)** for near objects, the ciliary muscles contract, the tension in the suspensory ligaments decreases, the lens becomes fatter, converging the light more

Reaction of the iris to changing light intensity

The iris consists of two sets of muscles, the CIRCULAR and RADIAL muscles, which work antagonistically (when one set contracts the other relaxes, see section 2.8) (Figure 2.4.8). They control the size of the PUPIL and so control the amount of light entering the eye.

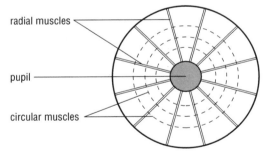

Figure 2.4.8 The iris seen from the front

Remember that when muscles contract they get shorter, so:

- In bright light the pupil gets smaller because the CIRCULAR MUSCLES CONTRACT and the RADIAL MUSCLES RELAX.
- In dim light the pupil gets larger because the CIRCULAR MUSCLES RELAX and the RADIAL MUSCLES CONTRACT.

Optical defects

People suffering from short sight or **myopia** are unable to see distant objects clearly. In short-sighted people the eyeball is usually too long from front to back. It can be corrected by wearing concave lenses that diverge the light (Figure 2.4.9).

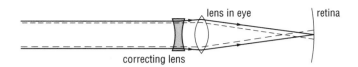

Figure 2.4.9 Correcting short sight

People who have long sight or **hypermetropia** have difficulty in focusing on nearby objects. This is caused by the eyeball being too short and is corrected by wearing convex lenses that converge the light (Figure 2.4.10).

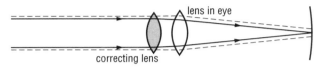

Figure 2.4.10 Correcting long sight

Quick Questions

1. Name the two parts of the nervous system.
2. Name the three types of nerve cell or neurone.
3. Name the junction between two neurones.
4. How are nerve impulses transmitted across this junction?
5. Using the terms stimulus, receptor, coordinator, effector and response, describe the iris reflex (change of pupil size).
6. Complete the table:

Stimulus	Receptor
Light	
	Ear
	Taste buds in tongue
Pressure/touch	

7. Name the functions in the eye of:
   a) the cornea;
   b) the sclera;
   c) the iris;
   d) the lens;
   e) the retina.
8. What shape is the lens when we are viewing
   a) Near objects?
   b) Distant objects?
   How is the change in shape brought about?
9. Name the two sets of muscles in the iris. How do they control the size of the pupil?
10. What are the differences between images formed by the rods and the cones?
11. What are:
   a) Short sight?
   b) Long sight?
   How are they corrected?

2.5 Hormones

The endocrine system is made up of a series of glands called ENDOCRINE GLANDS (see Figure 2.5.1). These glands are ductless glands; their chemical secretions (called **hormones**) pass directly into the blood and have an effect on another part of the body, the target organ or tissue.

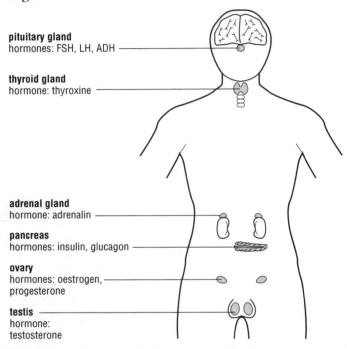

pituitary gland
hormones: FSH, LH, ADH

thyroid gland
hormone: thyroxine

adrenal gland
hormone: adrenalin

pancreas
hormones: insulin, glucagon

ovary
hormones: oestrogen, progesterone

testis
hormone: testosterone

Figure 2.5.1 The main endocrine organs and their hormones

The most important of these is the PITUITARY gland found just beneath the brain. Its secretions have effects on other parts of the body including all other endocrine glands and because of this it is sometimes referred to as the master gland.

Hormonal control of blood sugar

The PANCREAS monitors and controls the blood sugar level. Glucose is needed by all cells as a source of energy and must always be available to them. Levels of blood glucose do vary but only within narrow limits. The hormones involved are **insulin** and **glucagon** secreted by beta and alpha cells of the islets of Langerhans in the pancreas. The main target organ of these two hormones is the liver, in which the following reaction takes place:

$$\text{glucose} \rightleftharpoons \text{glycogen}$$

After a meal rich in carbohydrate the blood sugar is raised, and the pancreas responds by secreting more insulin. This lowers blood sugar by:

- Increasing uptake of sugar by cells.
- Stimulating liver cells to convert glucose to glycogen.

If blood sugar levels fall too low then the pancreas stops secreting insulin and starts secreting glucagon. This works in the opposite way to insulin, and glycogen is converted back to glucose thus increasing blood sugar.

Insulin control of blood glucose is an example of **negative feedback**. A high blood sugar level results in increased secretion of insulin. Insulin lowers the blood sugar level, which in turn reduces the rate of insulin secretion (Figure 2.5.2).

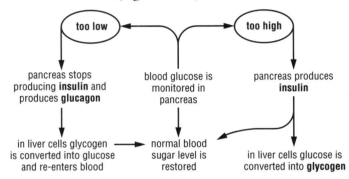

Figure 2.5.2 How hormones control blood glucose levels

Diabetes

Diabetes is a condition in which the blood sugar levels vary widely, leading to **hypoglycaemia** and **hyperglycaemia**. It is usually caused by the pancreas producing too little or no insulin. If blood sugar levels fall too low (hypoglycaemia) then cells, especially brain cells, cannot get enough glucose. This can lead to a coma. If too much glucose is present it causes damage to blood capillaries and the kidney. The body tries to get rid of the excess glucose and it is lost in urine, together with large amounts of water. One of the first signs of diabetes onset is excessive thirst and frequent urination. Diabetes is treated using control of diet, avoiding eating sugary foods and giving injections of insulin.

Hormones controlling reproduction

The sex organs (gonads) and the pituitary gland secrete the sex hormones. At the age of puberty (approximately 10 years old in females and 12 in males) the sex organs become active. The ovary starts to produce **oestrogen** and the testes produce **testosterone**, following release of **FSH** and **LH** from the pituitary. These hormones control the development of our secondary sexual characteristics. These include growth of body hair (males and females), deepening of the voice (males) and development of breasts (females).

Women have a **menstrual cycle**. Hormones from the pituitary and ovary control the monthly development of the uterus lining and release of an ovum. (Females are born with all the eggs – ova – they will produce in their lifetime. These are in an immature state in the ovary.) These hormones are:

- FSH is produced by the pituitary and causes an egg to mature in one of the ovaries. It also stimulates the ovaries to produce oestrogen.
- Oestrogen is secreted by the ovary as an egg develops. This causes the lining of the UTERUS (womb) to thicken and the blood supply to the uterus to increase in preparation for pregnancy, should it occur. When the oestrogen concentration in the blood reaches a certain level it will prevent further secretion of FSH by the pituitary, preventing more eggs from developing. Release of LH is also stimulated.
- LH is secreted by the pituitary and stimulates release of the egg (**ovulation**) around the 14th day of the menstrual cycle.
- **Progesterone** is secreted by cells left behind in the ovary (the CORPUS LUTEUM) after ovulation. It causes further thickening of the uterus lining. If the egg is not fertilised the corpus luteum stops producing progesterone and concentrations in the blood will fall. The uterus lining will begin to break down, and is lost together with a small quantity of blood (the menstrual flow or period). The cycle now begins again. If the egg is fertilised it will implant in the wall of the uterus and a PLACENTA will form. The placenta produces progesterone throughout pregnancy and it will promote continued development of the uterus and mammary glands. A complete menstrual cycle normally lasts for 28 days (Figure 2.5.3).

The role of hormones in controlling fertility

Some women may produce insufficient FSH and cannot therefore have a baby. By giving controlled amounts of FSH (as a fertility drug) to these women their eggs can be stimulated to mature.

Oestrogen may be used in oral contraceptives. It works by inhibiting FSH production so that no ova (eggs) mature.

Adrenalin

Adrenalin, the 'fight or flight' hormone, is produced by the ADRENAL GLANDS (found next to the kidney). It is secreted into the blood at times of stress, excitement and fright. Its role is to prepare the body for increased activity. It causes the heart to beat faster, and diverts blood to muscles and away from the skin, gut and kidneys. As a result more oxygen and glucose can be delivered to the cells so that the rate of respiration can be increased and therefore more energy released. These changes we feel as 'butterflies' in the stomach and cold clammy skin.

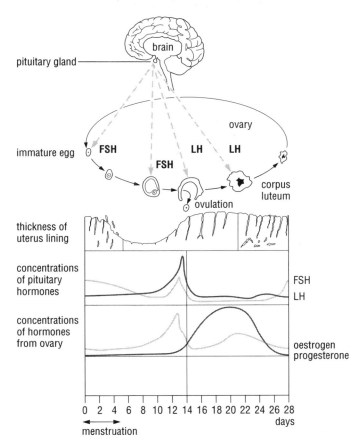

Figure 2.5.3 Changes in the ovary, uterus lining and hormone levels during a menstrual cycle

Quick Questions

1. What is a hormone?
2. What is the name of the endocrine gland that controls the activity of many of the other endocrine glands?
3. Name the endocrine gland that produces both insulin and glucagon.
4. What happens when the blood sugar level rises, e.g. after a meal?
5. What happens when blood sugar falls, e.g. between meals?
6. What is diabetes? How is it treated?
7. What hormonal changes occur at puberty?
8. During a normal menstrual cycle what happens to oestrogen levels between day 6 and day 14? Why do these changes occur?
9. What important event occurs around day 14? Which hormone triggers the event?
10. What hormone is produced by the corpus luteum in the second half of the cycle?
11. Why is FSH given to infertile women?
12. Why do oral contraceptives contain oestrogen?
13. What is the name of the hormone sometimes called the 'fight or flight' hormone?
14. How does this hormone prepare you for increased activity?

2.6 Homeostasis

To stay alive, animals and plants need to keep the conditions inside their bodies (their internal environment) relatively constant. **Homeostasis** is the maintenance of a constant internal environment.

Organisms can detect changes in their external and internal environment. As a result of these changes, nerve impulses or hormones are sent to organs which then respond to maintain a constant internal environment.

Which organs and organ systems are involved?

- The LUNGS are involved in controlling the oxygen and carbon dioxide content of the blood (see section 2.3, 'Breathing and respiration'). Water is also lost here.
- The KIDNEYS excrete metabolic waste products and maintain suitable **ion** and water levels in the blood.
- The SKIN and LIVER help to maintain the body at a suitable temperature.
- The SKIN is also involved with loss of water and ions.
- The LIVER and PANCREAS work on maintaining a suitable glucose level in the body (see section 2.5, 'Hormones').

The work of these organs is coordinated by the brain which must be continually informed of the conditions so that it can direct changes if necessary. In many cases negative feedback is involved.

The lungs

During exercise the level of carbon dioxide rises. This is detected by special receptors in the aorta and carotid artery (which is a branch off the aorta to the head), and also by receptors in the respiratory centre in the brain itself. The body responds by:

- Increasing the volume and number of breaths per minute.
- Increasing the number of heartbeats per minute and therefore circulating blood through the lungs at a faster rate.

These speed up the rate at which carbon dioxide is removed from the body. When carbon dioxide levels return to normal the body responds by:

- Returning the volume and number of breaths per minute to normal (Figure 2.6.1).
- Returning the number of heartbeats per minute to normal.

Water vapour is released during ventilation of the lungs.

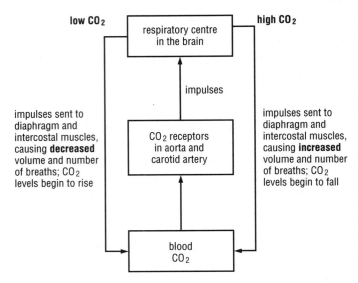

Figure 2.6.1 How the brain controls breathing rate

The kidneys

These are involved in homeostasis by excreting the excess or unwanted waste materials of metabolism. Especially important is the excretion of urea, which is made in the liver from surplus amino acids by a process called **deamination**.

The kidneys filter the blood at the rate of 1200 cm^3 every minute, removing waste and harmful substances together with a lot of water. We call this mixture urine. The urinary system is shown in Figure 2.6.2.

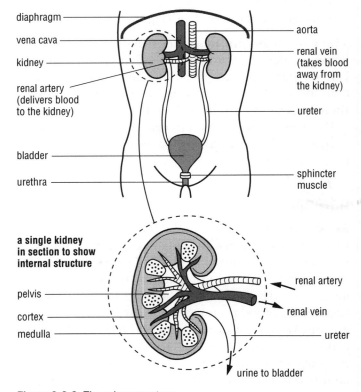

Figure 2.6.2 The urinary system

Table 2.6.1 Composition of urine

Waste substance	% by volume
Water	96
Urea (nitrogenous waste)	2
Salt	1
Other waste substances	1

Formation of urine

Each kidney contains over a million TUBULES or NEPHRONS. At one end of each tubule is a cup-shaped capsule called a BOWMAN'S CAPSULE (renal capsule). Within the capsule is a 'knot' of blood capillaries known as the GLOMERULUS. It is formed from the incoming arteriole (a small artery). The capsule is connected to a tube which twists and turns and leads to a COLLECTING DUCT (Figure 2.6.3). Associated with this tube are blood capillaries.

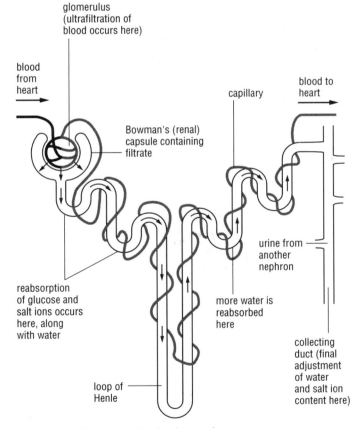

Figure 2.6.3 Production of urine in a nephron

Urine production involves two processes:

- ULTRAFILTRATION. Blood entering the glomerulus (already under high pressure from the pumping action of the heart) finds itself suddenly having to enter a narrower blood vessel. This raises the pressure inside the vessel to such an extent that some of the liquid in the blood passes out between the cells and into the cavity of the capsule. This liquid is known as a filtrate and contains useful substances, like glucose, as well as waste materials, like urea, in solution. Cells and proteins are left behind in the blood.

- SELECTIVE REABSORPTION. As the filtrate passes along the rest of the tubule/nephron, most of the valuable substances are reabsorbed back into the blood capillaries associated with it. By the time it arrives at the RENAL PELVIS the filtrate is known as urine.

In the kidney (Figure 2.6.4):

- Virtually all the urea is removed from the blood.
- Useful food molecules, such as glucose, are recovered from the filtrate before it becomes urine.
- Surplus salt and water are removed from the blood.

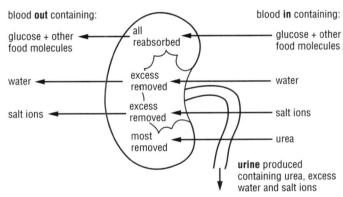

Figure 2.6.4 Production of urine in the kidney

The composition of urine varies according to:

- The protein content of the blood.
- Intake of water/liquid.
- Intake of salt.

Regulation of water content of blood (osmoregulation)

It is vital to balance water intake and output to ensure that the concentration of water in the blood and tissue fluid remains constant. Within the HYPOTHALAMUS of the brain are the OSMORECEPTORS which detect the water content of the plasma. If this is too low, the brain responds by sending impulses to the pituitary gland. This secretes the hormone **ADH** (antidiuretic hormone) into the blood. ADH reaches the kidney and makes the collecting duct wall more permeable to water. As a result more water can be reabsorbed from the urine back into the blood by osmosis. If there is too much water in the blood then less ADH is secreted by the pituitary, and therefore the collecting duct wall becomes less permeable to water and less water can be absorbed from the urine.

If it is very hot and we are producing a lot of sweat, the blood may become too concentrated. ADH will be secreted and more water will be absorbed by the collecting ducts. We will produce a small volume of concentrated urine.

If it is cold and we have been drinking a lot of fluid then the blood may become too dilute. ADH secretion will be reduced, and less water will be absorbed by the collecting ducts. We will produce a large volume of dilute urine.

This is another example of negative feedback. Low water concentration in the blood results in increased secretion of ADH. ADH causes more water to be reabsorbed; as the water concentration increases secretion of ADH is reduced.

Kidney failure, dialysis and transplants

If only one kidney fails, the other can usually perform the functions of both. If both kidneys stop working the waste substances they normally filter out of the blood start to build up, and if nothing is done death will quickly result. If both kidneys fail then a person's blood may be treated regularly using a DIALYSIS MACHINE, which restores the concentration of dissolved substances in the blood back to normal.

A dialysis machine removes the waste substances from the blood and adjusts its salt and water content, just as the kidneys would. It does this by a process called **dialysis**. In dialysis blood is removed from an artery, usually in the arm, and is passed over a dialysis membrane. On the other side of the membrane is a watery solution called DIALYSIS FLUID. This contains the normal concentrations of glucose and ions that are found in the body. As the blood passes over the membrane, waste substances diffuse out of it and into the dialysis fluid. The larger components of the blood such as the red and white blood cells are held back. The blood is eventually returned to the body through a vein in the arm. This process is continued until the blood has an acceptable composition (which could take up to 12 hours), and must be done two or three times a week. It is very uncomfortable to have to go through this every few days, and it causes great inconvenience and disruption in the person's life. In addition, between dialysis sessions toxins build up in the body perhaps causing damage to cells. The patient must eat a restricted diet that is low in protein and salt to reduce the risk.

Some people receive a healthy kidney from a donor. These transplant operations have several problems:

- Shortage of donors.
- Problems of tissue matching/typing.
- Rejection of the donor tissue (sometimes).
- Cost.

Kidney transplants versus dialysis machines

Advantages of a transplant:

- Can provide a permanent cure.
- Restores a normal lifestyle.
- The patient can have a normal diet.
- Less inconvenience for the patient.
- Less risk of infection (dialysis always carries a risk of infection).
- Cheaper in the long run.

Disadvantages of a transplant:

- Risk of rejection.
- Risk of complications due to surgery.
- Patient at risk following surgery due to use of IMMUNOSUPPRESSANT DRUGS.

Temperature regulation

Animals that can control their body temperature are called **endotherms**. They maintain a constant body temperature whatever the outside temperature. **Ectotherms** on the other hand have a body temperature that rises and falls with the outside temperature. Mammals, including humans, have a THERMOREGULATORY CENTRE in the brain (in the hypothalamus) in which can be found the temperature receptors. These monitor the temperature of the blood passing through the brain and can bring about changes in the body that will enable it either to conserve heat, if the blood temperature falls, or to lose heat, if the blood temperature rises. Human body temperature is normally 36.9 or 37°C. This is the optimum temperature for our enzymes to work. Above 41 °C they begin to denature; eventually they stop working altogether and death results.

In cold conditions:

- VASOCONSTRICTION occurs. The blood capillaries in the skin get narrower. As the lumen of the blood vessels get smaller there is reduced blood flow through these surface capillaries, so less heat is lost to the outside (Figure 2.6.5).
- Hair or fur is raised from the surface of the skin to trap an insulating layer of air next to it. This is done by the HAIR ERECTOR MUSCLES contracting and pulling the hair into a vertical position (causing goose pimples in humans).
- Skeletal muscle begins to contract and relax involuntarily (shivering), which helps to generate heat.
- Body metabolism may be speeded up and we eat more food.
- Behaviour changes and we may put on warm clothing or exercise more.

In hot conditions:

- VASODILATION occurs. Blood capillaries dilate (widen) so there is increased blood flow through surface capillaries and therefore more heat can be lost to the outside (Figure 2.6.5).
- Hair lies flat next to the skin as the hair erector muscles relax. This reduces the insulating layer of air.
- Sweating may start. The EVAPORATION of the sweat takes the heat energy away from the body as the water in the sweat changes from a liquid to a vapour.
- Metabolism slows down, so less heat is produced.
- Behaviour changes and we may wear less clothing and take cool drinks.

Hypothermia

In **hypothermia** the body temperature falls below 35 °C. It can be a problem for older people who live in poorly heated buildings and who may not eat properly. It also happens to people exposed to wet or very cold conditions for long periods of time. Enzyme activity is reduced, affecting most metabolic reactions in the body.

Hyperthermia

In **hyperthermia**, the body temperature rises to 40 °C, perhaps because of fever as a result of infection or heatstroke. Here the body fails to lose heat quickly enough as not enough water is drunk to replace that lost in sweating and so sweating stops. Failure to replace salt lost in the sweat causes dizziness and cramp.

Negative feedback

Temperature regulation is another example of negative feedback. Rising body temperature sets in motion mechanisms to increase heat loss and slow heat production. As the temperature falls these mechanisms are shut off.

Quick Questions

1 Define the term homeostasis.
2 How does the body respond to an increase or decrease in carbon dioxide concentration in the blood? Where is carbon dioxide concentration monitored?
3 What is urea? Where is it made?
4 What is ultrafiltration? Where does it occur and what is produced?
5 What is selective reabsorption? Where does it take place?
6 What are the differences in composition between the blood entering and leaving the kidney?
7 What is ADH? Where is it produced? What is its function?
8 What would be the effect on the volume and concentration of urine of drinking a lot of fluid on a cold day? Explain.
9 Explain why regulation of water content of the blood is an example of negative feedback.
10 If a person has kidney failure, how can they be kept alive?
11 What is normal body temperature for humans? Why must the body be kept at this temperature?
12 List the ways in which the body responds to a decrease in body temperature.
13 List the ways in which the body responds if the body temperature is too high.
14 What can happen to people if they are exposed to wet and cold conditions for a long time?

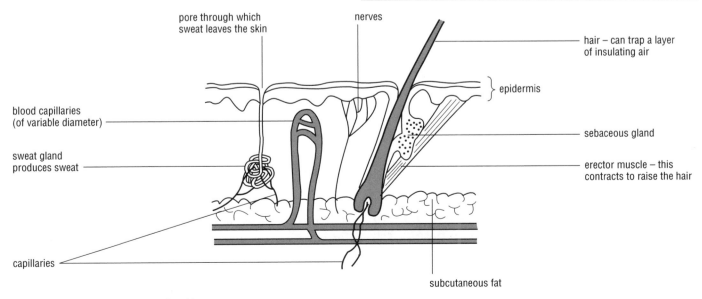

Figure 2.6.5 A section through the skin

2.7 Human reproduction

Structure and function of the reproductive organs

See Figures 2.7.1 and 2.7.2.

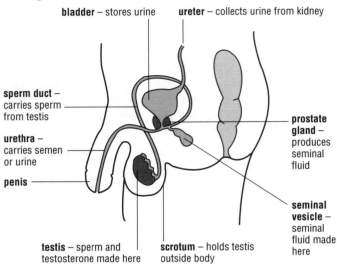

bladder – stores urine **ureter** – collects urine from kidney

sperm duct – carries sperm from testis

urethra – carries semen or urine

penis

prostate gland – produces seminal fluid

seminal vesicle – seminal fluid made here

testis – sperm and testosterone made here **scrotum** – holds testis outside body

Figure 2.7.1 The male reproductive system (side view)

Fertilisation

Fertilisation takes place in the OVIDUCT to produce a ZYGOTE. As a sperm penetrates the ovum (egg) membrane, the membrane changes to produce a barrier to prevent entry of more sperm.

The zygote then divides repeatedly by mitosis (see section 1.3), to produce a ball of cells. This implants in the lining of the uterus. A PLACENTA then develops which contains both maternal (mother's) and fetal blood vessels. It is here that exchange of materials occurs between mother and fetus. At the placenta oxygen and dissolved nutrients pass out of the maternal blood and enter the fetal blood by diffusion, and carbon dioxide and excretory products diffuse into the maternal blood. The maternal and fetal blood do not mix (Figure 2.7.3).

The developing fetus is surrounded by a fluid filled AMNIOTIC SAC. This acts as a shock absorber.

The placenta provides an effective but not a perfect barrier between maternal and fetal blood. The following are able to cross the placenta:

- Viruses such as **rubella** (German measles) and **HIV**. Contact with rubella can lead to deafness, heart defects, cataracts and mental retardation.
- Alcohol.
- Carbon monoxide from cigarettes. Babies born to mothers who smoke are usually born prematurely and underweight. They also stand a greater chance of developing **leukaemia**.
- Drugs, including paracetamol and 'recreational' drugs such as heroin and LSD.

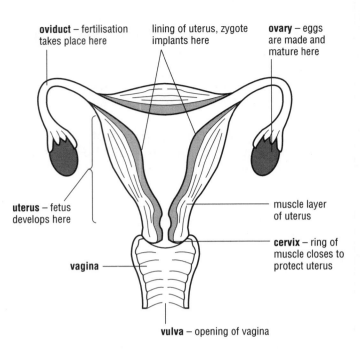

oviduct – fertilisation takes place here   lining of uterus, zygote implants here   **ovary** – eggs are made and mature here

uterus – fetus develops here

muscle layer of uterus

cervix – ring of muscle closes to protect uterus

vagina

vulva – opening of vagina

Figure 2.7.2 The female reproductive system (front view)

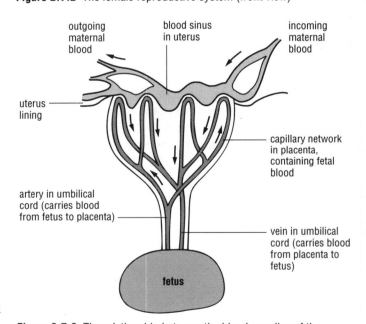

outgoing maternal blood   blood sinus in uterus   incoming maternal blood

uterus lining

capillary network in placenta, containing fetal blood

artery in umbilical cord (carries blood from fetus to placenta)

vein in umbilical cord (carries blood from placenta to fetus)

fetus

Figure 2.7.3 The relationship between the blood supplies of the mother and the fetus in the placenta

Birth

The period of pregnancy (gestation) is approximately 40 weeks. When the birth process begins, the muscles of the uterus contract pushing the baby towards the cervix. The muscles of the cervix dilate to allow the baby to pass through. Eventually the amniotic membrane ruptures and the fluid is lost. When the cervix is fully dilated the baby's head and shoulders appear first, the rest of its body soon following. The last stage involves contraction of the muscles of the uterus to remove/eject the placenta.

Multiple births

Identical twins occur when division of a single fertilised egg (zygote) produces two identical groups of cells. These develop into two genetically identical individuals.

If a female releases two or more ova and they are all fertilised then this will give rise to a multiple birth – twins, triplets and so on. The individuals are not genetically identical and may be of different genders.

Infertility

There are several possible causes, including:

- Low sperm count in males.
- Non-production of mature eggs in females.
- Blocked oviducts.
- Miscarriage, abortion due to hormonal imbalance.

New techniques now exist to increase the chances of successful pregnancy.

1 Fertility drugs like FSH and LH can be given to stimulate the ovary to produce mature eggs. Unfortunately, this can lead to multiple ovulations.
2 *In vitro* fertilisation is fertilisation carried out outside the mother's body. Fertile eggs are extracted from the mother and fertilised using either the father's or a donor's sperm. This technique is often carried out following the use of fertility drugs.
3 The embryos produced by *in vitro* fertilisation can be returned to the uterus of the mother. This is called **embryo transplantation**. Following fertility treatment and *in vitro* fertilisation there may be several viable embryos. Some will be transplanted and some can then be stored in liquid nitrogen.

Contraception

Natural methods

The RHYTHM METHOD involves females making a careful study of their menstrual cycles. On the day of ovulation body temperature rises slightly. By taking the temperature every day for several months a pattern should emerge. If the female does not have sexual intercourse for approximately seven days around the expected day of ovulation, pregnancy should not occur. This method of contraception carries a fairly high risk of pregnancy.

Mechanical methods

These include:

- The sheath or condom. This should be placed on an erect penis before sexual intercourse. It traps sperm and therefore prevents fertilisation.
- The intra-uterine device (IUD). This is a small plastic coil or loop with copper wrapped around it. It is inserted into the uterus by a doctor and prevents implantation of a zygote.
- The diaphragm (dutch cap). This is placed over the cervix by the woman before sexual intercourse. It prevents entry of sperm into the uterus.

Chemical methods

These include:

- Spermicides. These are chemicals contained in creams, foams and gels which kill sperm. They should be used with condoms and diaphragms. On their own they are of limited contraceptive value.
- Contraceptive pills. These contain oestrogen and progesterone at concentrations that prevent development of any eggs/ova in the ovary. As a result ovulation cannot take place.

Surgical methods

These involve cutting and sealing either the oviducts or the sperm ducts.

Sexually transmitted diseases

These are diseases passed from one person to the next during sexual intercourse. They include:

- **Gonorrhoea**, which is caused by a bacterium. Symptoms include a burning sensation on urination and yellow discharge from the penis or cervix. If untreated, it can lead to sterility. It is easily treated using antibiotics but unfortunately resistant strains of the bacterium are appearing.
- HIV (human immunodeficiency virus), which suppresses the patient's immune response. Diseases that would normally be successfully dealt with by the immune system can be fatal. Patients commonly die of pneumonia and rare forms of cancer.

Quick Questions

1 What is the function of
  a) The testes?
  b) The sperm duct?
2 Where does fertilisation take place?
3 Where does implantation of the fertilised egg (zygote) occur?
4 What is the function of the placenta?
5 Name two substances/organisms that can cross the placenta.
6 What leads to the birth of
  a) Identical twins?
  b) Non-identical twins?
7 What hormones are given to stimulate ovulation in infertile females?
8 How do contraceptive pills prevent pregnancy?
9 Give two examples of sexually transmitted diseases.

2.8 Exercise and health

The skeleton

The skeleton:

- Provides support and protection for soft delicate organs such as the brain (cranium) and heart (rib-cage).
- Provides a framework for muscles to attach to, allowing movement and locomotion.
- Produces red and white blood cells (in the bone marrow).

The human skeleton consists of:

- The skull or cranium and the vertebral column (axial skeleton).
- The pelvic and pectoral girdles, to which the limbs are attached.
- The rib-cage and sternum.

Most of the adult skeleton is made of bone, a hard tissue containing cells, which is impregnated with minerals such as calcium carbonate and calcium and magnesium phosphates. Bone also contains protein fibres. Before birth most of the bones of the human fetus are made of cartilage. This is a firm yet elastic tissue. The cartilage skeleton is progressively OSSIFIED, that is, hardened by deposits of calcium phosphate. This process is not complete at birth, which means that the skeleton can continue to grow. A band of cartilage is found at both ends of the bone (Figure 2.8.1). This continues to grow and as it does so it becomes ossified so that the bone continues to increase in length.

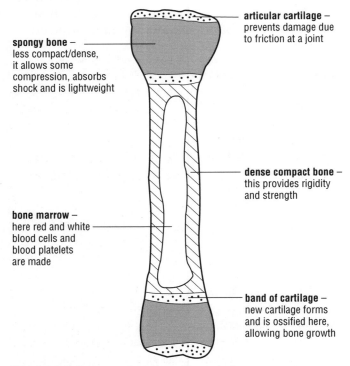

Figure 2.8.1 Structure of a bone (still growing)

spongy bone – less compact/dense, it allows some compression, absorbs shock and is lightweight

articular cartilage – prevents damage due to friction at a joint

dense compact bone – this provides rigidity and strength

bone marrow – here red and white blood cells and blood platelets are made

band of cartilage – new cartilage forms and is ossified here, allowing bone growth

Joints

These occur where two or more bones meet. At a joint where bones rub together, the ends of the bones are covered with a slippery layer of articular cartilage to reduce wear and tear. There are several types of joint:

- Fixed – for example, between the bony plates of the skull, the bones of the pelvic girdle (hip) and between the pelvic girdle and vertebral column. These joints allow very little or no movement.
- Freely movable joints (synovial) joints (Figure 2.8.2) which include:
  - Hinge joints, such as the elbow, knee and digit joints. Here movement in one plane (direction) only is possible.
  - Ball-and-socket joints, such as the shoulder and hip joints, where movement can occur in all planes (directions).

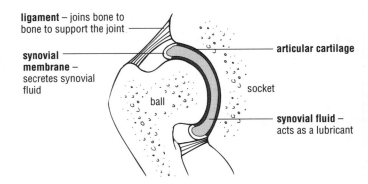

ligament – joins bone to bone to support the joint

synovial membrane – secretes synovial fluid

articular cartilage

socket

ball

synovial fluid – acts as a lubricant

Figure 2.8.2 A synovial joint (ball-and-socket type)

In synovial joints the membrane in the joint secretes a fluid known as SYNOVIAL FLUID. This acts as a lubricant to reduce friction and helps the joint to move freely.

Muscle tissue

There are three types of muscle tissue:

- Cardiac muscle, found only in the heart.
- Smooth or involuntary muscle, so called because it is not under the control of the will or conscious part of the brain. Examples include the muscles around the gut and the muscles of the iris.
- Skeletal or voluntary muscle, so called because it is under our conscious control. This is involved with the movement of the skeleton.

The properties of muscle include:

- When muscles contract, they shorten and thicken.
- Muscles only contract when nerve impulses reach them.

- Muscles have a good blood supply to provide the oxygen and glucose needed for aerobic respiration, which releases the energy needed for the contraction. The more vigorous the contraction, the more energy is needed. In addition the blood removes the excess carbon dioxide and excess heat produced during vigorous exercise. Lactic acid is removed during anaerobic respiration.
- Muscles can only contract. A muscle must be stretched or relaxed indirectly by the action of another muscle acting on the skeleton in the opposite direction. This explains why muscles are usually found in pairs – their action being opposite and equal, that is ANTAGONISTIC ACTION.

The antagonistic action of muscles can be illustrated using the forearm. The main muscles involved are the BICEPS or FLEXOR muscle, which bends the arm, and the TRICEPS or EXTENSOR muscle, which straightens the arm. Both are attached to bone by inelastic, strong tissue called TENDONS (Figure 2.8.3).

Limbs act as levers. The muscle supplies the force, the weight of the bone plus anything extra (such as an object in the hand) acts as the load and the joint is the pivot or fulcrum.

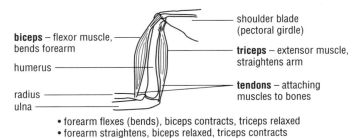

- forearm flexes (bends), biceps contracts, triceps relaxed
- forearm straightens, biceps relaxed, triceps contracts

Figure 2.8.3 Movement of the forearm

Tendons and ligaments

Ligaments are bundles of tough, strong yet slightly elastic fibres which join bone to bone. Their slight elasticity allows some movement at joints, but they prevent bones from separating.

Tendons are also very strong and attach muscle to bone. Unlike ligaments they are inelastic, which means that when muscles contract the tendons 'pull' the bone and bring about movement. Tendons must be strong to ensure that muscle stays firmly attached to the bone.

Effects of exercise on performance

Care should be taken during exercise to avoid:

- Sprains, which occur when the ligaments and other tissues are torn, often as a result of a sudden or severe overload or wrench.
- Dislocations, which occur when a bone is forced out of its joint.

Regular exercise will improve and maintain performance by:

- Keeping the muscles toned.
- Keeping the tendons supple.
- Keeping the joints working smoothly.
- Maintaining an efficient supply of blood to the heart and lungs.

There is an important relationship between heartbeat, breathing and exercise. Increased activity increases the rate (number of breaths per minute) and depth (volume of air in each breath) of breathing. The number of heartbeats per minute and the STROKE VOLUME (volume of blood per beat) also increases. The flow of blood increases to muscles but decreases to non-vital areas like the skin and gut. These changes in blood flow have two effects:

- Increased oxygen and glucose supply to the muscle cells.
- Increased removal of carbon dioxide and other waste products (such as lactic acid) from muscle cells.

Regular exercise (training) decreases both resting pulse rate and blood pressure. This is because of the increased stroke volume of the heart at rest. Regular exercise increases the vital capacity of the lungs. This means more oxygen is transferred to the blood at each breath. One way of determining a person's fitness is by calculating how long it takes his or her pulse rate to return to normal after a limited period of exercise. The greater the fitness, the faster the pulse rate will return to normal.

Quick Questions

1 What are the functions of the skeleton?
2 What is bone made of?
3 What is the skeleton of an unborn baby made of at first?
4 What is the function of bone marrow?
5 What is the function of articular cartilage?
6 Give an example of a fixed and a freely movable joint.
7 In a synovial joint, what is the function of the synovial fluid?
8 Muscles are often said to work antagonistically. Explain what this means.
9 In what ways are tendons and ligaments
   a) Similar?
   b) Different?
10 What is the difference between a sprain and a dislocation?
11 What is the effect of exercise on the heart and breathing?
12 What is the effect of regular training on pulse rate, vital capacity, tendons and muscles?

2.9 Disease

Disease or ill health is any disorder or malfunction of normal body functions. There are many causes:

- Diseases caused by other living organisms, often microorganisms. These are called INFECTIOUS DISEASES, for example influenza or measles.
- INHERITED DISEASES caused by genetic disorders, such as cystic fibrosis (see section 5.2).
- Diseases caused by environmental conditions. These are often INDUSTRIAL DISEASES. Emphysema, caused by working or living in an atmosphere polluted by high concentrations of dust particles, is an example.
- Diseases caused by AGEING, such as arthritis. This is seen as loss of mobility at joints due to damage to the articular cartilage. In osteoporosis the bones become brittle due to lack of minerals like calcium.
- Human-induced or LIFESTYLE DISEASES, caused by smoking, drinking excess alcohol, using solvents or recreational drugs or steroids. Included here are also dietary diseases, such as obesity.

Diseases caused by microorganisms (infectious diseases)

A variety of microorganisms can cause disease:

- Viruses. These are the smallest and can only reproduce inside living cells. Influenza and the common cold are caused by viruses. AIDS is caused by the human immunodeficiency virus (HIV).
- Bacteria. These are larger than viruses. Diseases caused by them include *Salmonella* food poisoning, tuberculosis (TB) and cholera.
- Fungi. These are non-green, non-animal organisms. Fungal diseases include athlete's foot, ringworm and thrush.
- Protozoa. These are microscopic single-celled organisms (belonging to the Kingdom Protoctista). Malaria is caused by this type of microorganism.

Details of the structure and multiplication of these organisms are dealt with in section 7.1.

Microorganisms that cause disease are called **pathogens**. Disease will occur if these pathogens gain entry to the body either as a result of unhygienic conditions or by contact with infected people. Once inside the body the pathogens multiply, either inside or outside body cells. As a result, cells may be damaged or destroyed, either directly or by the release of TOXINS. The overall effect is that normal metabolic processes are hindered or stopped. The body's fitness is reduced as resources are diverted towards defending it. A common symptom of this is a high body temperature or fever.

The spread of disease

Microorganisms can be spread (transmitted) in various ways:

- In the air, by droplet infection. Viruses such as the influenza virus and the TB bacterium can be carried in droplets of mucus from the nose and mouth (coughing and sneezing). Disease spreads more quickly if people live or work in overcrowded conditions.
- By contaminated water. If drinking water is contaminated with waste water (sewage) containing urine and faeces then diseases, such as cholera, are spread rapidly through a community.
- By food contaminated as a result of unhygienic storage and handling or inadequate cooking. Not washing hands after using the toilet, or storing raw meat and cooked meat together, may result in *Salmonella* food poisoning.
- By direct contact with an infected person or their body fluids, as with sexually transmitted diseases like AIDS.
- By other animals which act as **vectors**. For instance, mosquitoes take blood infected with the protozoan that causes malaria from one person and can transmit the organism to a non-infected person the next time they take a blood meal.
- By the unhygienic disposal of household rubbish. This encourages possible carriers of disease (vectors), like flies and vermin (e.g. rats), to visit or live close to where people live. An example is the transmission of Weil's disease (leptospirosis) by rats.

The control and prevention of disease

Infectious diseases can be controlled or prevented by:

- Boosting the body's natural defences (immunisation).
- Eliminating the disease-causing organism or its vector.
- Avoiding contact with the disease-causing organism or with infected people.
- Treating the disease in its early stages.

Immunisation

Immunising large numbers of people against a particular disease, such as TB, smallpox or measles, can control the spread of disease and save lives. In the case of measles it may prevent long-term harm, such as blindness, deafness and brain damage, which can result from the disease. Immunisation has led to the eradication of smallpox worldwide. For more about immunisation see section 2.10.

Eliminating the pathogen or its vector

If the pathogen needs a vector to complete its life-cycle and be transmitted from one person to another, then if we eliminate the vector we can reduce the spread of disease. An example of this is the attempt to control malaria by draining streams and ponds in which the eggs of mosquitoes are laid and develop. Insecticides can be sprayed on the walls of houses to kill the adult mosquitoes.

Many potential vectors of disease, like houseflies and rats, feed on or around household waste. Therefore safe hygienic disposal of household waste is essential.

- Household waste should be stored in suitable metal or plastic containers with lids heavy enough to prevent animals getting in.
- Containers should be lined (now usually with black plastic bags) and washed occasionally.
- Waste should be collected regularly and frequently using special refuse-collection vehicles.

The collected waste can then be dealt with in two ways:

- Removal to landfill sites (refuse tips). These should be at least one mile from residential areas.
- Incineration (burning in purpose-built furnaces).

There are advantages and disadvantages to both methods (Table 2.9.1).

Table 2.9.1 Waste disposal methods

Advantages	Disadvantages
Landfill	
Cheap	Still attracts possible vectors
Unusable land can be reclaimed	Many sites are needed and areas of ecological importance are now being used
Incineration	
Valuable land is not used	Incinerators are expensive to build and run
Since waste is destroyed vectors are not attracted	Incinerators produce toxic fumes
Heat produced can be used to generate energy	The water table may become contaminated

Storage and handling of food

This is an important area for the elimination of pathogens (or preventing their reproduction). Human food needs to be protected from organisms that cause food poisoning, for example *Salmonella*, *Campylobacter* and *E. coli*. In addition it needs to be protected from organisms that 'spoil' food. These are decomposers like the fungi that grow on food, such as the 'mould' on bread.

The chances of food poisoning can be dramatically reduced if simple food safety rules are followed. These include:

- Regular washing of hands especially after using the toilet and when preparing food.
- Keeping flies, cockroaches and rodents away from food.
- Keeping raw meats away from cooked meats.
- Thorough cleaning of work surfaces and kitchen equipment before and after use.
- Thorough cooking of meats (particularly chicken) and meat products.
- Thorough thawing of frozen food before cooking.
- Identifying 'carriers' of microorganisms. These people have the microbes in their bodies but do not show symptoms of the disease.
- Preventing 'carriers' of disease from working in the food industry.

The *Salmonella* bacterium is the most common cause of food poisoning. It results from eating chicken, eggs or other meat that is contaminated and inadequately cooked. It is impossible to eradicate the organism as it is found in most farm animals and particularly in their faeces. Moreover, modern farming practices make it more likely that animals are infected, for example, 'battery' hens stand on or close to their own faeces.

Extending the natural life of food

We can store and preserve food so that micro-organisms are killed, or at least cannot multiply. This means that the food remains safe to eat for longer periods of time. The main methods used are:

- Refrigeration: food is cooled and kept between 0 °C and 5 °C. This slows down the rate of reproduction of the microorganisms.
- Deep freezing: food is cooled to -18 °C to -24 °C. This prevents the growth of microorganisms.
- Drying (dehydration): water is removed from the food. Water is needed by all living organisms for enzyme action, so growth is prevented if it is absent. Food like fish may be dried in the sun; milk is freeze-dried to make skimmed milk powder.
- Osmotic preservation (using sugar or salt): if high concentrations of sugar or salt are added to food then water will be drawn out of the cells of the microorganisms by osmosis. The bacteria cannot reproduce since enzyme activity is prevented. Jams and meats such as ham and bacon are preserved in this way.

- Canning or bottling: the food is cooked/heated to about 90 °C and then placed, still hot, into cans or jars and sealed. As the food cools it contracts and a vacuum develops. Conditions become anaerobic and most bacteria are unable to multiply.
- Irradiation: the food is exposed to ionising radiation so that most of the microorganisms are destroyed, that is, the food is sterilised. There is still a danger that the food may contain toxins which could cause disease.
- Pasteurisation: this is used for liquids such as beer and milk. The liquid is heated to 72 °C for 15 seconds and then cooled rapidly to 10 °C. This kills most bacteria, including *Salmonella* and the TB bacterium, without affecting the taste of the treated food.
- Ultra-heat treatment (UHT): this is a way of sterilising milk. It is heated to 132 °C for 1 minute, killing almost all microorganisms, and then cooled rapidly.

Treatment of water

See section 7.2 for details of the treatment of sewage.

Water taken from rivers and reservoirs has to be made safe to drink. The process has several steps (Figure 2.9.1):

- SCREENING: this removes debris such as sticks and fish.
- SEDIMENTATION, or settling: large solid impurities settle to the bottom of the sedimentation tank.
- FILTRATION: the water trickles over layers of sand, fine gravel, coarse gravel, small stones and large stones. Any suspended organic matter is digested and decomposed by saprophytic microorganisms. Most pathogens are removed at this point by protozoa.
- CHLORINATION: chlorine is added to kill any remaining bacteria. Fluorides may also be added (which reduce the risk of tooth decay).
- STORAGE: the water is stored in covered water towers or reservoirs, from which it can be pumped to houses.

Avoiding contact with the disease-causing organism

This is particularly important for those diseases transmitted by contact with an infected person, their belongings or their body fluids. Using condoms can reduce the spread of sexually transmitted diseases such as AIDS, for example.

In the case of diseases such as TB, patients are isolated from other people; any person who might have been infected is contacted and tested for the presence of the organism.

The spread of athlete's foot is reduced by avoiding sharing towels.

Treating disease in its early stages

If diseases such as TB and meningitis are diagnosed and treated early, there is a greater chance of a full recovery and risk of permanent damage is reduced.

The body's methods of defence

Non-specific methods

- The skin is a tough, impermeable barrier and most microorganisms cannot penetrate it. They can gain access via cuts, however, or via natural openings such as the nose or mouth.
- Mucus is produced in many parts of the body. In the respiratory system, for example, sticky mucus is produced which traps microorganisms. The mucus is then moved up to the back of the throat by cilia and swallowed.
- Hydrochloric acid in the stomach kills most microorganisms taken in via the mouth.
- Phagocytosis (Figure 2.9.2): 75% of the white blood cells are of a type known as phagocytes. These are able to engulf and digest almost any microorganism.

Specific methods

Here another type of white blood cell called a LYMPHOCYTE is involved. Lymphocytes produce specific proteins known as ANTIBODIES and ANTITOXINS, which destroy invading microorganisms as well as the toxins produced by them. This process is called the IMMUNE RESPONSE. Details of this are in section 2.10.

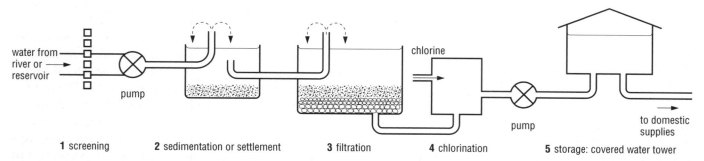

Figure 2.9.1 Treatment of drinking water

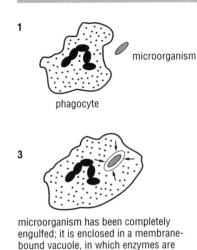

1    microorganism

phagocyte

2   phagocyte detects microorganism and begins to engulf it

3   microorganism has been completely engulfed; it is enclosed in a membrane-bound vacuole, in which enzymes are secreted to destroy the microorganism

4   action of enzymes has destroyed the microorganism

Figure 2.9.2 Phagocytosis

Lifestyle-related factors

Drugs are substances that alter the chemical processes in people's bodies so that the way the body works is changed. Most drugs are taken to make people who are ill feel better. Some are taken to change a person's mood, however, and people can become dependent on them or addicted to them and suffer withdrawal symptoms without them. Many 'lifestyle-related diseases' are caused by the use or misuse of drugs. They can lead to long-term physical damage. Some drugs are injected into the body using hypodermic needles. If people share these or use dirty ones, then they are at risk from diseases like HIV and hepatitis.

Smoking

Tobacco smoke increases the risk of diseases such as lung cancer, emphysema and bronchitis. The nicotine in cigarettes is a drug which reaches the brain in only 30 seconds. It causes an increase in heart rate and blood pressure. It may cause irregular heartbeats and an increased risk of disease of the heart and blood vessels. Blood is also more likely to clot, thus increasing the risk of strokes and thromboses. High levels of carbon monoxide will reduce the amount of oxygen carried in the blood to the body's cells.

Alcohol

Alcohol has a direct effect on the central nervous system. It slows down our reactions, impairs our judgement and may lead to loss of consciousness. It also acts as a depressant. The long-term effects include permanent damage to the cells of the brain and liver.

Solvents

These include glue, lighter fuel and aerosol spray vapours. In the short term they cause a change in behaviour, due to hallucinations. In the long term they can damage the skin, brain, liver and kidneys.

Anabolic steroids

These drugs may be taken by sportsmen and women to improve muscle development and therefore performance. Their harmful side-effects include damage to liver cells and increased aggressive behaviour; in females, menstrual cycles may become irregular or stop.

'Recreational' drugs

A wide range of drugs are used to change the 'mood' of a person. They include LSD, ecstasy, heroin and cannabis. They all affect the central nervous system and will cause changes in behaviour. Their long-term effects include liver, kidney and brain damage. They, or impurities mixed with them, may cause death due to kidney failure, dehydration and blood poisoning.

Quick Questions

1 What are the five main causes of disease in humans?
2 What are the four main types of microorganism that cause disease?
3 List the six main methods by which disease is spread. Name a disease spread by each method.
4 Explain how pathogens cause disease once they are inside the body.
5 List the four main ways in which disease is controlled and prevented. Give named examples of diseases controlled by each method.
6 a) Which organism is the most common cause of food poisoning?
   b) List the ways in which we can reduce the risk/spread of food poisoning.
   c) Why have modern farming practices made it more likely that animals are infected with *Salmonella*?
7 List the eight main ways of preserving (extending the natural life) of food. Give a named example of a food preserved by each method.
8 List the five main stages in the treatment of water supplies to produce drinking water.
9 List the four main non-specific methods of defence against microorganisms.
10 Name the type of white blood cell involved in a specific immune response. What chemicals do they produce?
11 Why are drugs of all kinds dangerous if misused?
12 What are the effects on the body of
   a) Tobacco smoke and tar?
   b) Nicotine?
13 What effect does alcohol have on the body?
14 What are the effects of solvent abuse:
   a) In the short term?
   b) In the long term?
15 What are anabolic steroids? What are the harmful side-effects of their misuse?

2.10 Biotechnology and disease

Medicines contain useful drugs. Some, like painkillers such as paracetamol, can only help to relieve the symptoms of disease. Others, like antibiotics, can be used to cure diseases by preventing bacteria multiplying or destroying them.

Antibiotics

Antibiotics can only be used to attack bacteria. They are useless against other microbes like viruses, which live and reproduce inside cells. This makes viruses difficult to destroy without damaging the body's cells and tissues.

Many antibiotics are produced by fungi; PENICILLIN, for example, is produced by the fungus *Penicillium*. However, STREPTOMYCIN is produced by the bacterium *Streptomyces*. See section 7.2 for details of antibiotic manufacture.

Many antibiotics, including penicillin, prevent the manufacture of a cell wall in a wide range of bacteria. This prevents them from multiplying, so their action is called BACTERIOSTATIC. Others may cause the destruction of the cell membrane of the bacteria causing their death. This action is called BACTERICIDAL.

In recent years overuse and misuse of antibiotics has lead to the development of antibiotic-resistant strains of bacteria. Those bacteria that show mutations giving them antibiotic resistance are selected for by natural selection. Eventually whole new 'strains' of resistant bacteria develop (see section 5.3).

The effectiveness of different antibiotics can be compared by placing discs of paper containing different antibiotics on to an agar plate inoculated with harmless bacteria (Figure 2.10.1). See section 7.1 for details about preparing agar plates.

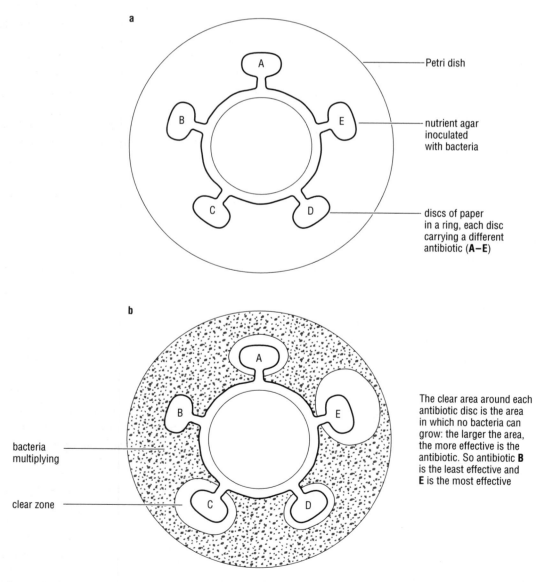

a

— Petri dish

— nutrient agar inoculated with bacteria

— discs of paper in a ring, each disc carrying a different antibiotic (**A–E**)

b

bacteria multiplying

clear zone

The clear area around each antibiotic disc is the area in which no bacteria can grow: the larger the area, the more effective is the antibiotic. So antibiotic **B** is the least effective and **E** is the most effective

Figure 2.10.1 Comparing the effectiveness of antibiotics: (**a**) agar plate at the start of the experiment, (**b**) the agar plate after 24–36 hours

How the body's immune response works

All cells carry antigens (usually made of protein) on their surface. These antigens are specific to a particular organism, such as the TB bacterium or the polio virus. If FOREIGN antigens (antigens found in a body which did not produce them) enter the body, they will be recognised by lymphocytes. The lymphocytes mount an immune response to the foreign antigen. They may produce antibodies which will destroy antigens (Figure 2.10.2), or they may release antitoxin.

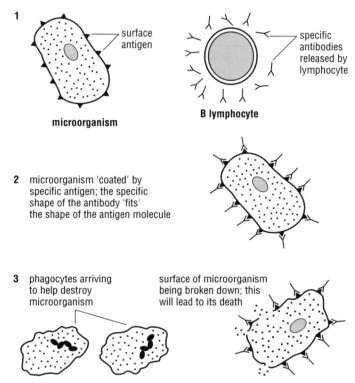

Figure 2.10.2 The role of lymphocytes in the immune response

There are two types of lymphocyte:

- T LYMPHOCYTES: these carry antibody molecules on their surface that can recognise foreign antigens, attach to them and bring about the destruction of cells, including any of our own cells that are infected by viruses.
- B LYMPHOCYTES: these secrete (release) specific types of antibody and respond to freely circulating antigens and toxins in the plasma, such as the TB bacterium.

When they encounter a foreign antigen both types of lymphocyte are stimulated to divide rapidly to form a clone of cells (genetically identical), most of which produce a specific type of antibody.

The first time the body encounters (detects) a new foreign antigen the immune response is slow; this is a primary response. During the immune response some of the clone cells go on to form MEMORY CELLS. These

can respond much more quickly the next time the same antigen is met. We say the body has built up an IMMUNOLOGICAL MEMORY and this is dependent on the presence of specific B and T memory lymphocytes. If these are present the response (production of antibodies) is so rapid that no symptoms of disease will be seen. This is called the secondary response. For example, we show symptoms of many childhood diseases like chicken pox and measles on our first exposure but afterwards we are immune. Immunological memory is highly specific to the antigen involved.

The immune response is very specific, and antibodies for one antigen will not protect us against a different antigen. Also some antigens, including 'colds' and influenza viruses, occur in a variety of different strains, with slightly different antigens. This explains why we catch colds repeatedly.

The immune response may occur naturally through infection or can be induced artificially by immunisation.

Immunisation

Passive immunity

Immediate protection can be gained when a person has been exposed to a dangerous disease like tetanus or rabies, by injecting them with antibodies against the antigen which have been made by another organism. Since the antibodies have not been made by the individual this protection is called PASSIVE IMMUNITY. It is not permanent because no memory lymphocytes have been made.

Active immunity

This is achieved by giving a person a vaccine (by mouth or by injection). The vaccine contains small quantities of the microorganism, or antigens from its surface. The vaccine is treated to ensure it is unable to cause the disease but will protect against infection by that specific microorganism. The result is that the lymphocytes respond by producing specific antibodies that will defend the body against a future attack by the same type of invading organism. This type of immunity is referred to as ACTIVE IMMUNITY as the body has actually made its own antibodies.

How are vaccines produced?

There are five ways in which they can be produced:

- Using the killed VIRULENT (disease-causing) pathogen. Whooping cough vaccine is made in this way.
- Using a live NON-VIRULENT (non-disease-causing) strain of the pathogen, as for tuberculosis and rubella (German measles) vaccines. A live virulent culture of the microorganism is SELECTIVELY SUBCULTURED for many generations in the laboratory.

This means that the least effective (at causing disease) pathogens of each generation are selected out and cultured again and the most virulent are destroyed. At each stage therefore a weaker (less able to cause disease) strain is produced. Finally it is possible to produce a strain that cannot cause disease, even though it can multiply in the body.

- Separating the antigens from the pathogen and using them as a vaccine (for example, influenza vaccine).
- Chemically modifying a toxin molecule, such as tetanus or diphtheria toxin, so that it is no longer toxic but still resembles the toxin antigenically.
- Using genetically engineered bacteria or other microbes such as fungi to mass produce the relevant antigen; a vaccine against hepatitis B virus is made in this way (see section 5.2).

The risks of immunisation

There is a risk attached to being given a vaccine. Some people have an abnormal or allergic reaction as a side-effect, and may develop raised temperature or a rash. In very rare cases encephalitis (inflammation of the brain) can occur, causing permanent brain damage. However the risks of immunisation are much less than the risk of death or permanent damage associated with diseases such as tetanus, measles and polio.

Organ transplants

Sometimes it is possible to replace diseased or damaged organs, such as the kidney, heart and liver, with healthy ones from a donor. The transplanted organ is treated as foreign and may be REJECTED by the person receiving it, as their lymphocytes can recognise the foreign antigens and will start producing antibodies against it. In order to prevent rejection:

- A donor with a 'tissue type' similar to that of the recipient is used. The antigens of the donor's cells are compared with the antigens of the recipient's cells; if they are very similar, then the transplant is less likely to be rejected.
- The blood-producing areas in the recipient (the bone marrow) may be IRRADIATED to slow down the production of white blood cells.
- The recipient is kept in STERILE conditions for some time after the operation to reduce the risk of infection. This is necessary because their number of white blood cells is low following irradiation or the use of drugs.
- The recipient is treated with IMMUNOSUPPRESSANT drugs which maintain a low rate of production of white blood cells. More recent immunosuppressant drugs target specifically the T lymphocytes that are mainly involved in rejection.

Blood transfusions

The most commonly 'transplanted' tissue is blood and it is vital that rejection does not take place.

Red blood cells carry specific antigens on their surface. These allow us to classify blood into various groups. The most important type of blood grouping system is the ABO system, which depends on the presence or absence of antigens known as A, B and O antigens. Table 2.10.1 shows the type of blood group, the antigens present and also the antibodies found in the plasma of different types of individuals.

Table 2.10.1 Blood group types

Blood group	Antigens present	Antibodies present
A	A	b
B	B	a
AB	AB	(neither a or b)
O	(neither A or B)	a and b

In a blood transfusion it is important that the blood of the recipient and donor are COMPATIBLE. This means that transfusion of blood will be safe. If the antibodies present in the recipient's blood can attach to the antigens on the red blood cells of the donor, then the antibodies will cause the red cells to stick together and AGGLUTINATION will occur (do not confuse this with blood clotting, which is a different process). If agglutination occurs it can lead to blockage of small blood vessels and perhaps death. Table 2.10.2 shows which blood can be given to recipients of different blood groups. In blood transfusions THE ANTIBODIES OF THE DONOR CAN BE IGNORED BECAUSE OF THE DILUTION EFFECT.

Table 2.10.2

Donor blood type	Recipient blood type			
	A	B	AB	O
A	+	−	+	−
B	−	+	+	−
AB	−	−	+	−
O	+	+	+	+

Key: + = transfusion possible
− = transfusion not possible

The use of monoclonal antibodies

Antibodies are very specific, that is, each antibody will only attach to a specific antigen. Therefore they can be used to target specific cells. It is hoped that monoclonal antibodies may be able to help in the fight against disease, including cancer. If one type of antibody (a monoclonal antibody) that is specific to the antigens of one type of cell can be mass produced in the laboratory, then diseases of those cells can be targeted. For example, an anticancer drug could be attached to a monoclonal antibody that is specific to the type of cell affected by the cancer.

The monoclonal antibodies are made by CLONING and culturing specific lymphocytes in the laboratory. Since the lymphocytes are clones they will all be producing the same type of antibody, which can be collected.

Disinfectants and antiseptics

These are chemicals used to kill microorganisms, or at least reduce their number. Neither is able to kill bacterial spores and therefore they do not produce sterile conditions.

Disinfectants are usually used for kitchen surfaces, floors and toilets. They are highly toxic to microorganisms but should not be used to clean wounds or rashes. Examples of disinfectants include phenol and hypochlorite solutions.

Antiseptics are designed to kill microorganisms without damaging human cells, and can therefore be used to clean wounds and prepare the skin for surgery. Examples include alcohol and chlorhexidine.

We can compare the effectiveness of disinfectants and antiseptics by exposing bacteria on an agar plate to different preparations. If we leave the agar plates for the same length of time in the same conditions, we can compare the numbers of bacteria that survive (Figure 2.10.3). The more effective the chemical, the fewer bacteria that will survive.

Figure 2.10.3 Comparing the effectiveness of disinfectants

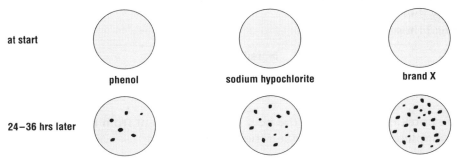

Three Petri dishes with nutrient agar; inoculated with the same bacteria and equal volumes of different disinfectants

The more colonies of bacteria there are, the less effect the disinfectant has in preventing growth of bacteria. So phenol is the most effective and brand X the least effective in this comparison.

Quick Questions

1. Name two antibiotics in common use.
2. How do antibiotics help to cure us of diseases caused by bacteria?
3. What problem facing doctors is due to overuse of antibiotics?
4. What are antigens and antibodies?
5. Describe briefly what happens when a microorganism enters the body.
6. Why is a secondary immune response much faster than a primary response?
7. Why is it unlikely that we will suffer from diseases like chicken pox more than once?
8. In what two ways can immunity be induced artificially?
9. What are the five ways in which vaccines are made?
10. What are the risks attached to immunisation?
11. Transplanted organs such as kidneys can be 'rejected' – what does this mean?
12. In what ways can we reduce the risk of organ rejection?
13. If incompatible donor blood is transfused into a recipient, what happens and why?
14. Complete Table 2.10.3.

Table 2.10.3

Donor blood group	Recipient blood type			
	A	B	AB	O
A				
B				
AB				
O				

Key: + = transfusion works
− = transfusion fails

Section Two: Examination Questions

1. This question is about digestion.
   Enzymes in the mouth, stomach and small intestine help to digest food.
   (a) What do enzymes do to food during digestion? [1]
   (b) What must then happen to the **digested** food before it can be used by cells in different parts of the body? Explain as fully as you can. [3]
   (c) Glucose (sugar) is one of the foods used by body cells. What is the glucose used for? Explain as fully as you can. [2]

   (MEG (Suffolk), Merit, June 1996)

2. Sam bought some tins of soup. A tin of tomato soup had the following information on its label.

Nutritional information	
	Amount per 100 g
Energy	243 kJ
Protein	10.0 g
Carbohydrate	7.0 g
Fat	3.0 g
Fibre	0.5 g
Sodium	0.5 g

Ingredients
Water, tomatoes, sugar, modified cornflour, dried skimmed milk, salt, spices.

   (a) (i) Work out the total amount of protein, carbohydrate, fat, fibre and sodium in 100 g. [1]
       (ii) Explain why this total is not 100 g. [1]
   A tin of beef soup had these ingredients.

Ingredients
Water, beef, animal fat, vegetable oil, salt, spices.

   (b) How would the nutritional content of the beef soup be different from the tomato soup?
   To show this, complete the table by ticking the boxes.

Nutritional contents	More than tomato soup	About the same as tomato soup	Less than tomato soup
Protein			
Carbohydrate			
Fat			

   (c) (i) Write down **one** reason why we need to eat **protein**.
       (ii) Write down **one** reason why we need to eat **carbohydrate**.
       (iii) Write down **one** reason why we need to eat **fat**. [3]
   (d) This is a diagram of the human digestive system. Label the diagram. [4]

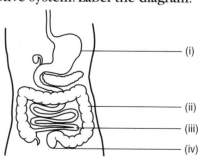

   (e) Write down **one** job that the large intestine does. [1]

   (MEG (Suffolk), Merit, June 1996)

3. The diagram shows a section through the heart.

right side   left side

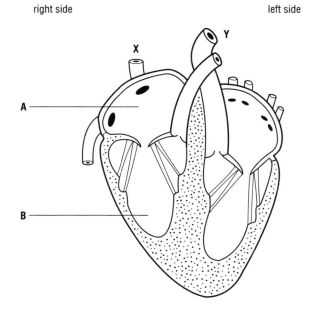

(a) Label the parts **A** and **B**. [2]
(b) Describe in detail the passage of the blood through the heart from **X** to **Y**. Include reference to valves, vessels and any other organs involved. [7]

(WJEC, Higher, Specimen)

4. Look at the diagram. It shows an alveolus (air sac) in the lungs.

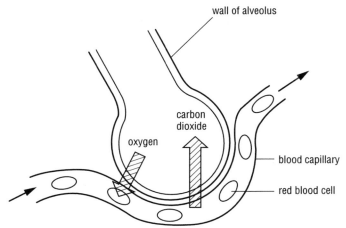

Gas exchange happens in the alveoli (air sacs).
(a) Alveoli are adapted for efficient gas exchange. Write down **three** ways they are adapted for this. [3]
Carbon dioxide passes from the blood into the alveoli.
(b) (i) Where, in the body, is this carbon dioxide made? [1]
    (ii) What process produces this carbon dioxide? [1]
(c) How is the level of carbon dioxide in the blood controlled? Answer the question by completing these sentences.
    High levels of carbon dioxide are detected by ....
    Signals are sent to the diaphragm and rib muscles to increase the rate of ....
    This causes the level of carbon dioxide in the blood to ....
    This system of control is called .... [4]

(MEG (Suffolk), Special, June 1996)

5. The figure below shows how oxygen demand and supply (intake) change during exercise.

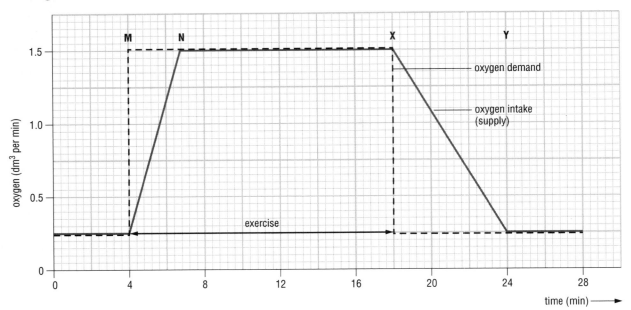

(a) (i) Explain why oxygen demand starts to rise as soon as exercise starts. [2]
    (ii) Why does it take some time for oxygen supply to meet oxygen demand? [2]
    (iii) How may 'warming up' before a race help an athlete during the period **M–N**? [1]
    (iv) Complete the word equation for **aerobic** respiration.
        glucose + ... → .... + ... + ATP [2]
    (v) What is the other product formed by anaerobic respiration in muscle cells? [1]
(b) Explain why the oxygen supply has to exceed the oxygen demand during the period **X–Y**. [2]

(MEG (Salters), Higher, Specimen)

6. While preparing for a long race athletes are advised to have a diet which consists mainly of carbohydrate before a race. The carbohydrate in the diet should be starch.
(a) Describe what would happen to the starch in the athlete's digestive system. [2]
(b) The graph shows the effect of high-carbohydrate diets on the stored carbohydrate in the muscles.

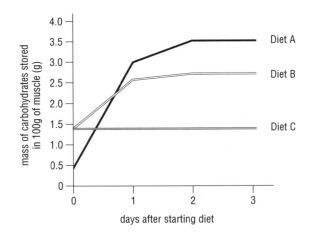

Diet A – High-carbohydrate diet, started after several days of eating a diet **without** carbohydrate.
Diet B – High-carbohydrate diet, started after normal mixed diet.
Diet C – Normal mixed diet.
    (i) Explain how the stored carbohydrate would help an athlete during a long race. [3]
    (ii) What advice would you give the athlete about the best diet preparation for a long race? Explain why you would give this advice. [2]

(NEAB, Level Q, June 1995)

7. In an investigation two groups of trained athletes ran ten short sprints as fast as possible. One group had been trained as sprinters, the other as long-distance runners. Between each sprint they rested for half a minute. The total period of exercise with rests lasted 5.5 minutes. The graphs show the maximum running speed and the changes in lactic acid concentration in the blood for each group during and after the exercise period.

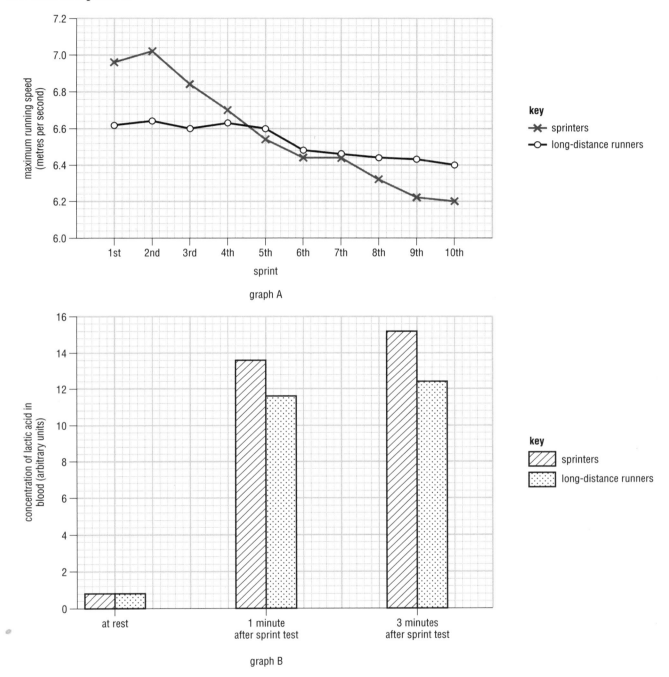

graph A

graph B

(a) Give **two** conclusions that can be drawn from Graph A about the differences between the sprinters and the long-distance runners. [2]

(b) What happens to the lactic acid concentration in the blood in the 3 minutes after exercise? Suggest a possible reason for this. [2]

(c) What would have happened to the lactic acid concentration after a further 10 minutes rest? Explain why. [2]

(d) The rate of oxygen uptake during exercise was found to be greater for the long-distance runners than for the sprinters. Suggest how this could explain the differences in lactic acid concentrations between the two groups. [4]

(NEAB, Higher, Specimen)

8. The diagram below shows a section through an eye.

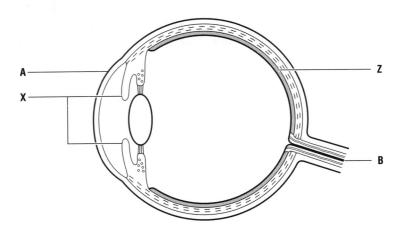

(a) Name the parts **A** and **B** [on the lines provided].   [2]

(b) On the diagram, put a **C** on the part which focuses light by changing shape.   [1]

(c) If a bright light shines on the eye, structure **X** will change shape due to a reflex action. Describe this change.   [3]

(d) Tissue **Z** contains two types of light-sensitive cell. Name the two types of cell and state the function of each type.   [2]

(e) The diagram below shows a simple reflex arc.

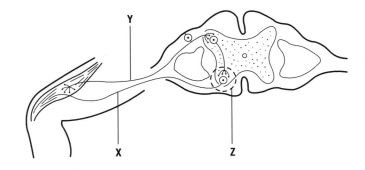

Label structures **X** and **Y** [on the lines provided].   [2]

(f) The diagram below shows some of the details of region **Z**.

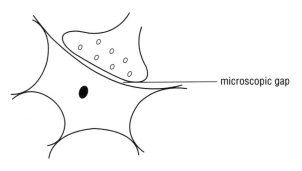

microscopic gap

(i) Name the microscopic gap shown in the diagram above.   [1]

(ii) Describe how nerve impulses are transmitted across this gap.   [3]

(London Double Award, Higher, Specimen)

9. When a reflex action takes place, it can be summarised as follows:

1 Stimulus → 2 Receptor → 3 Coordinator → 4 Effector → 5 Response.

Give an example of a reflex action and describe it in terms of **1–5** above.   [5]

(WJEC, Higher, Specimen)

10. Read the following passage, which is from an advice book for diabetics.

Insulin reactions

Hypoglycaemia, or 'hypo' for short, occurs when there is too little sugar in the blood. It is important always to carry some form of sugar with you and take it immediately you feel a 'hypo' start. A hypo may start because:

- you have taken too much insulin, or
- you are late for a meal, have missed a meal altogether, have eaten too little at a meal, or you have taken a lot more exercise than usual.

The remedy is to take some sugar.

An insulin reaction usually happens quickly and the symptoms vary - sweating, trembling, tingling of the lips, palpitations, hunger, pallor, blurring of the vision, slurring of speech, irritability, difficulty in concentration.

Do not wait to see if it will pass off, as an untreated 'hypo' could lead to unconsciousness.

(a) Many diabetics need to take insulin.
  (i) Explain why. [2]
  (ii) Explain why there is too little sugar in the blood if too much insulin is taken. [3]
  (iii) Explain why there is too little sugar in the blood if the person exercises more than usual. [3]
(b) Suggest why sugar is recommended for a 'hypo', rather than a starchy food. [3]
(c) Explain how the body of a healthy person restores blood sugar level if the level drops too low. [3]
(d) Explain, using insulin as an example, what is meant by negative feedback. [3]

(NEAB, Level R, June 1996)

11. The graph below shows the relative levels of two hormones, oestrogen and hormone **Q**, during a woman's menstrual cycle.

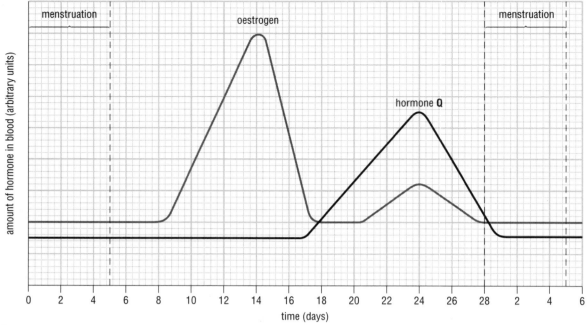

(a) When is the level of oestrogen equal to the level of hormone **Q**? [2]

(b) What effect does the build up of oestrogen have from day 9 to day 14? [2]

(c) (i)   Name hormone **Q**. [1]

(ii) In which part of the body is hormone **Q** produced? [1]

(iii) Which event is caused by a fall in the level of hormone **Q**? [1]

(iv) What would be indicated if the high level of hormone **Q** continued beyond day 24? [1]

(London Double Award, Higher, Specimen)

12. (a) The diagram shows part of the control system involved in the female reproductive cycle.

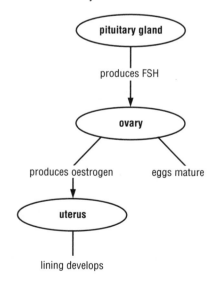

(i)   What type of substance are FSH and oestrogen? [1]

(ii) How does FSH get from the pituitary gland to the ovary? [1]

(b) High levels of oestrogen inhibit the production of FSH by the pituitary gland.

(i)   Explain how this is an example of negative feedback. [2]

(ii) One drug that is used to treat female infertility is clomiphene. Clomiphene blocks the inhibitory effect of oestrogen on FSH production. Explain how this may help in the treatment of infertility. [2]

(NEAB, Higher, June 1997)

13. The diagram below shows a single kidney tubule.

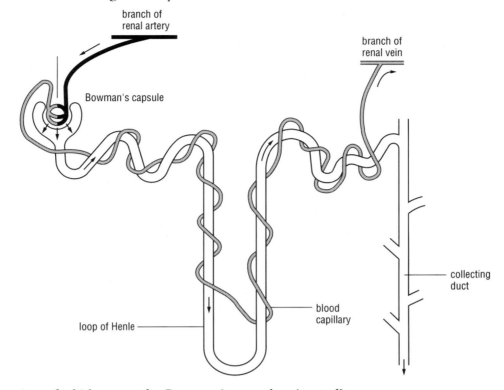

(a) In which region of a kidney are the Bowman's capsules situated? [1]

(b) Explain why the liquid trickling down the loop of Henle does **not** contain glucose even though the Bowman's capsule does. [1]

(c) Name the liquid in the collecting duct. [1]

(d) In which part is filtration taking place? [1]

(WJEC, Higher, Specimen)

14. (a) Briefly explain how the kidney produces urine. [5]

(b) The diagram shows a kidney machine that is used to return blood plasma to its normal composition.

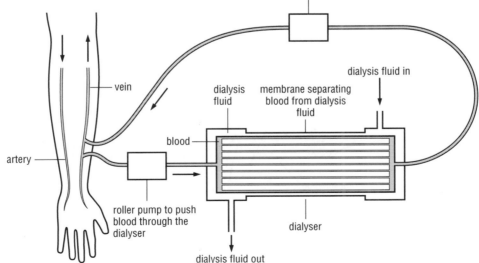

(i) Give **one** way in which the dialysis fluid entering the machine would be different from the patient's blood plasma. [1]

(ii) Give **two** ways in which the dialysis fluid entering the machine would be the same as the patient's blood plasma. [2]

(NEAB, Higher, Specimen)

15. (a) Describe how the amount of water in the body is controlled by the kidneys. [3]
  (b) In the treatment of kidney failure:
   (i) Give **two** possible advantages of using a kidney transplant rather than a dialysis machine.
   (ii) Give **two** possible disadvantages of using a kidney transplant rather than a dialysis machine. [4]

(NEAB, Level R, June 1996)

16. The diagram shows a vertical section of human skin.

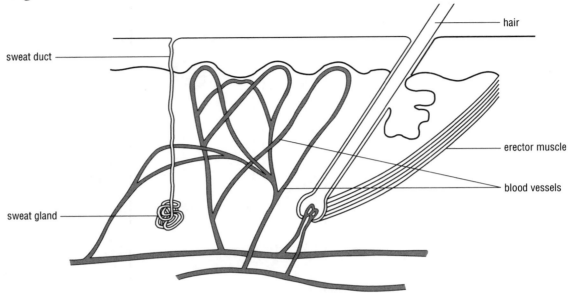

Explain **two** ways that human skin helps to control body temperature. [6]

(SEG Double Award, Higher, Specimen)

17. (a) The diagram shows the events leading to implantation.

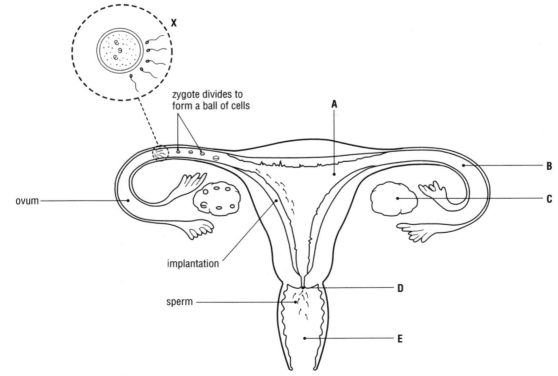

   (i) Name parts **A**, **B**, **C**, **D** and **E**. [5]
   (ii) Name the process occurring at **X**. [1]
   (iii) What is meant by implantation? [2]

(continued)

(b) The diagram shows a fetus just before birth.

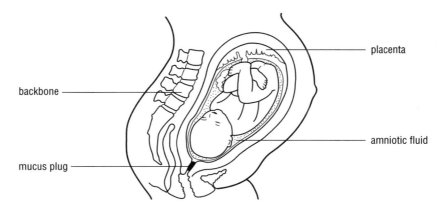

(i) Give **two** functions of the amniotic fluid. [2]
(ii) Give **two** ways the diagram shows that the fetus is ready for birth. [2]
(iii) Explain the roles of the cervix and uterus during birth. [4]

(c) (i) Complete the boxes by choosing a word to describe how each contraceptive method works:

Chemical	Mechanical	Natural	Surgical

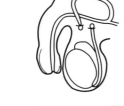 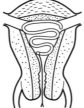 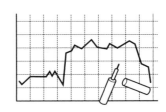

sterilisation	intra-uterine device	rhythm method

[3]

Some over-populated countries have introduced sterilisation programmes.
(ii) Suggest **two** reasons why this method of contraception is used for such programmes. [2]

(CCEA, Level Q, June 1997)

18. (a) The diagram shows a fetus just before birth.

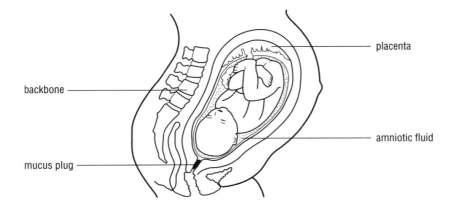

(i) Give **two** functions of the placenta. [2]
(ii) Why does the placenta have a large surface area? [1]
(iii) Suggest why the maternal and fetal circulations must be separate. [2]

(continued)

(b) The diagram shows changes in the uterus and the daily body temperature during the menstrual cycle.

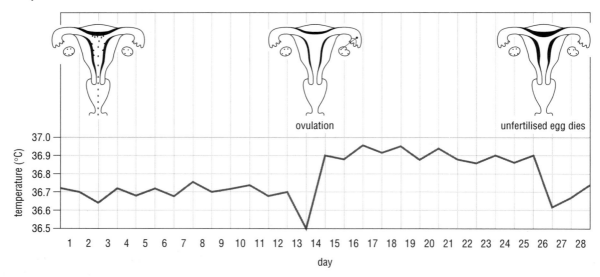

(i) What is happening in the uterus between days 1 and 5? [1]

(ii) How does the lining of the uterus change between days 14 and 26? [1]

(iii) Explain what is happening during ovulation, on day 14. [2]

(iv) Explain how this information can be used as a method of contraception. [2]

(v) Give **two** reasons why this method of contraception could be unreliable. [2]

(c) A cause of infertility is when the ovary fails to produce eggs. In such cases fertility drugs containing a hormone, which stimulates egg production, may be taken.

(i) Name the hormone which stimulates egg production. [1]

(ii) Suggest why this treatment may result in multiple births. [2]

Another cause of infertility is blocked oviducts.

(iii) Explain how *in vitro* fertilisation could overcome this and help a couple produce a child. [3]

(CCEA, Level R, June 1997)

19. The diagram shows a cross-section of a long bone from a partially grown child.

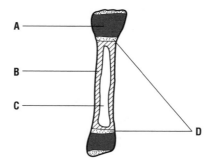

(a) Four types of tissue found in bones are labelled in the figure. Put the correct letter **A**, **B**, **C** or **D**, beside each tissue type.

(i) Bone marrow. ⬜   (ii) Dense compact bone. ⬜

(iii) Cartilage. ⬜   (iv) Spongy bone. ⬜ [3]

(b) Which of the features labelled on the diagram will disappear after the bone is fully grown? [1]

(c) Explain the function of:

(i) Spongy bone. [2]

(ii) Bone marrow. [2]

(MEG (Salters), Higher, Specimen)

20. The diagram shows the bones and muscles in the upper part of the arm and the shoulder blade.

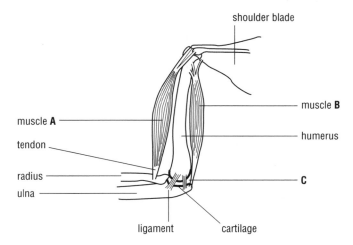

(a) What is the name of the fluid in the space labelled **C**? [1]
(b) (i) Which muscle will cause the lower part of the arm to move up when it contracts? [1]
    (ii) Explain why this movement of the lower part of the arm occurs when the muscle contracts. [2]
(c) Both tendons and ligaments are made of very strong tissues. Tendons are not elastic but ligaments have elastic tissue in them. Explain how these features are important in the working of the elbow joint. [4]

(SEG, Human Biology, Foundation, Specimen)

21. Choose the correct words from the list in the box below to complete each of the following sentences.

animals bacteria fungi protozoa viruses

(a) Influenza is a common disease caused by .... [1]
(b) Diphtheria is caused by .... [1]
(c) Ringworm is caused by .... which live in the skin. [1]

(SEG Human Biology, Foundation, Specimen)

22. (a) The diagrams show a bacterium and a protozoan.

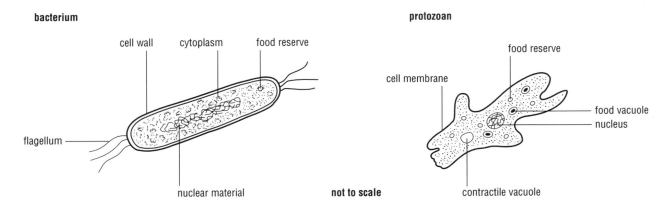

    Describe as accurately as possible **four** ways in which these two are different as shown only in the diagrams. [4]
(b) Ringworm is caused by a fungus.
    (i) Give **one** external structural feature of such a fungus. [1]
    (ii) Describe **one** way by which a person may become infected with ringworm [2]
(c) Influenza is a disease easily spread from one person to another. Explain how the disease is spread so easily. [2]

(SEG Human Biology, Higher, Specimen)

23. The diagram below shows how long milk stays fresh at different temperatures.

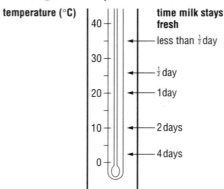

Use the information in the diagram to answer the following questions.
(a) At which temperature will the milk stay fresh for only one day? [1]
(b) Suggest how you could keep milk fresh for three days. [1]
(c) What is the effect, on the time for which milk stays fresh, of each 10 °C increase in the storage temperature between 0 °C and 40 °C? [2]

(London, Foundation, Specimen)

24. Landfill tipping and incineration are two methods used for the disposal of household rubbish. Complete the table below by giving **two** advantages and **two** disadvantages of each method.

	Advantages	Disadvantages
Landfill tipping	1	1 ....
	2	2 ....
Incineration	1	1 ....
	2	2 ....

[8]

(SEG, Foundation, Specimen)

25. This headline and table appeared in a newspaper article.

Schoolchildren risk health with heavy drinking
How much schoolchildren drink in a week

Amount drunk (units of alcohol*)	Aged 11 (%)	Aged 12 (%)	Aged 13 (%)	Aged 14 (%)	Aged 15 (%)
None	75.7	64.1	56.7	44.7	31.4
1–6 units	20.1	29	29.7	34.2	38.8
7–10 units	1.7	3.5	5.4	8.8	13.3
11–14 units	1.6	1.4	3.7	5.2	5.4
15–20 units	0.7	1	2.1	3.8	4.6
21+ units	0.3	1	2.4	3.3	7.5

(*One unit = half a pint of beer/one glass of wine/one measure of spirit)

(a) (i) Calculate the percentage of 13-year-old children who drink more than 10 units of alcohol per week. Show your working. [1]
(ii) Calculate how many pupils this would be, on average, in a year group of 180 13-year-old pupils. Show your working. [2]
(b) 14-year-old Elaine was asked why she drank alcohol. She said, 'I think it helps you to unwind when you get home from school, or if you've had a really bad day.' Suggest how alcohol has this effect. [2]

(NEAB, Tier R, June 1995)

26. Microorganisms may get into the blood. The drawing shows some of the ways in which they are dealt with by white blood cells.

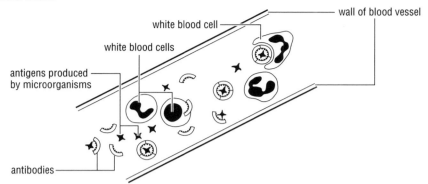

(a) Using only the information in the drawing, explain how microorganisms are destroyed in the blood.

[5]

(b) Humans can be protected against certain diseases by vaccination.

When vaccinated against tuberculosis (TB) a person is given an injection of very **weakened** but still **living** TB bacteria.
- (i) Why are **weakened** bacteria used? [1]
- (ii) Why are **living** bacteria used? [1]
- (iii) After the vaccination the person will be immune to TB for many years. Explain why. [2]

(c) In preparing anti-tetanus serum, the microorganisms which cause the disease in humans are first injected into another animal. Any person thought to be infected with tetanus is given an injection of serum prepared from the blood of this animal.

Explain why the injection of this serum will destroy quickly any tetanus microorganisms in the person's blood but the effects of the serum do **not** last for very long. [2]

(SEG, Higher, Specimen)

27. (a) (i) What is meant by the term **antigen**? [1]
(ii) Which part of a virus contains antigen? [1]

(b) There is a relationship between the presence of HIV (the human immunodeficiency virus) and the development of AIDS. The graphs below show the relationship between the number of helper T cells (a type of lymphocyte) and the amount of HIV antigen present in the blood of an infected person.

key
— helper T cells
- - HIV antigen

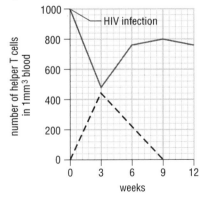

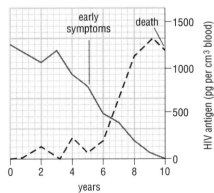

(adapted from *New Scientist*, 13 June, 1992)

- (i) The graphs have been drawn using two different time scales. Suggest why this was done. [1]
- (ii) Describe the relationship shown on the graphs between the amount of HIV antigen and the number of helper T cells in the blood. [1]
- (iii) Helper T cells help other lymphocytes of the immune system.
  Use this information, the information in the graphs and your own knowledge, to suggest the causes of death in AIDS sufferers. [4]

(c) (i) What is meant by **secondary response** to antigen? [1]
(ii) How is a secondary response made possible? [1]
(iii) What is the importance of the secondary response? [1]

(London, Higher, Specimen)

28. **(a)** Give **three** ways in which white blood cells help to defend us from infective microbes. [3]
    (b) Explain why antibiotics can be used to treat bacterial infections, but are not used to treat viral infections. [2]
    (c) Immunisation helps to protect us from disease.
      (i)   Explain why immunisation with the dead infective microbes protects us from disease. [2]
      (ii) Give **three** ways of producing vaccines, **other** than using dead infective microbes. [3]

      (NEAB, Higher, Specimen)

29. Blood of group **A** was added to plasma from group **B** blood in a dish and mixed well. After a short time the following reaction was seen.

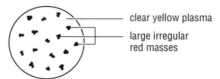

— clear yellow plasma
— large irregular red masses

Describe as fully as possible what happened to cause this change in appearance of the blood. [4]

      (SEG Human Biology, Higher, Specimen)

30. Ann investigated the effect of three types of antiseptic mouthwash **A**, **B** and **C**. She grew bacteria from her mouth in three Petri dishes. She then added equal amounts of mouthwash to each Petri dish. The dishes were covered and left for 24 hours. The diagrams below show the Petri dishes at the start and after 24 hours.

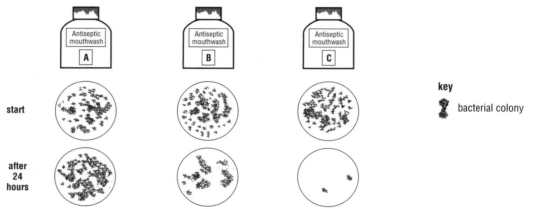

(a) Which mouthwash had the best effect? Give a reason for your answer. [2]
(b) What effect did mouthwash **A** have on the bacteria? [1]
(c) Give **two** harmful effects which the bacteria in Ann's mouth could have. [2]
(d) Give **one** way, apart from using a mouthwash, to improve mouth hygiene. [1]

      (London, Foundation, Specimen)

31. Work surfaces in a kitchen may be sterilised by cleaning with a sodium hypochlorite solution. You are provided with the following materials and apparatus.

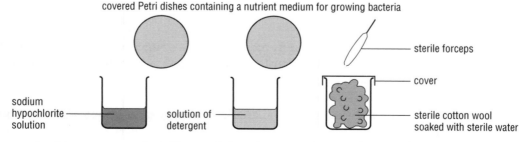

covered Petri dishes containing a nutrient medium for growing bacteria

— sterile forceps
— cover
sodium hypochlorite solution
solution of detergent
— sterile cotton wool soaked with sterile water

You are asked to compare the effects of cleaning a surface with an ordinary detergent and with a sodium hypochlorite solution on bacterial numbers. Describe precisely an experiment you could do using the materials and apparatus shown above. [5]

      (SEG Human Biology, Higher, Specimen)

Section
THREE

Patterns in other organisms

3.1 Patterns of feeding

All living organisms require a source of food to provide energy. Green plants are able to manufacture their own organic molecules (glucose, for example). They are called **autotrophs**. Animals, fungi and bacteria are **heterotrophs**, meaning that they cannot make their own organic food molecules and they therefore depend on green plants for these molecules.

Specialised feeding in mammals

Herbivores

Herbivores eat plants. Cellulose cell walls are difficult to digest and therefore we see specialised dentitions (teeth) and digestive systems in herbivores. Their teeth are designed to allow efficient grinding of plant material (Figure 3.1.1). They have well-developed PREMOLARS and MOLARS with ridges for grinding; CANINES are absent and sheep and cows have no upper INCISORS. Their jaws move from side to side.

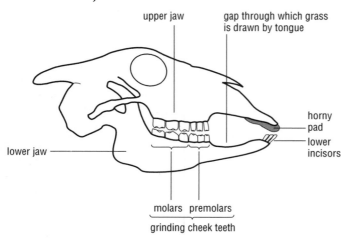

Figure 3.1.1 An example of herbivore dentition (sheep)

Many herbivores rely on bacteria living in their digestive system to help to digest plant material. Cows, for example, have one stomach divided into four chambers. The RUMEN contains bacteria that break down the cellulose. When cows swallow grass it passes into their rumen where it is mixed with the cellulose-digesting bacteria that begin its digestion. The mixture in the rumen is then regurgitated into the mouth to be chewed again (commonly known as chewing the 'cud'). The process is repeated many times.

Carnivores

These are meat-eaters. In these animals the incisors are used to scrape meat from the bone and pull meat apart. The canines are used to hold and kill the prey. The premolars and molars form large CARNASSIAL TEETH which slide past each other, crushing bones and

cutting meat like a pair of scissors (Figure 3.1.2). Their jaws can only move up and down and not from side to side.

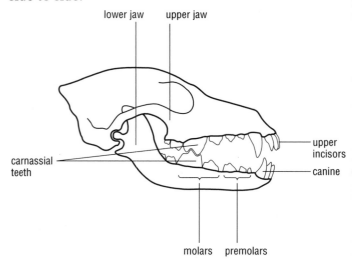

Figure 3.1.2 An example of carnivore dentition (dog)

Animals that feed on fluids or by filtering fluids

Many insects are 'fluid feeders' and they have specialised mouthparts (Figure 3.1.3). Some have mouthparts which are long and sharp, like hollow needles. Mosquitoes, for example, are able to pierce the skins of animals and suck blood from surface capillaries. Greenfly or aphids take in a sugary solution from the phloem of plants.

Other fluid feeders digest their food by releasing saliva containing enzymes on to it and then sucking up the liquid produced (this is known as EXTRACELLULAR digestion). Houseflies feed in this way and this explains why they are important vectors of disease-causing bacteria.

Butterflies and moths feed on the sugary nectar of flowers. They have a hollow tube-like PROBOSCIS, which is coiled when not in use.

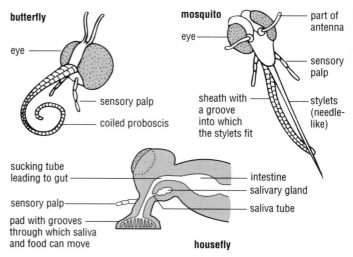

Figure 3.1.3 Fluid feeders

Animals that live in water can filter particles of food from it. A wide range of animals feed in this way, including some whales, fish and shellfish (mussels, Figure 3.1.4). Most of these animals feed on microscopic organisms called PLANKTON (ZOOPLANKTON and PHYTOPLANKTON). Water containing the food is drawn into the animal. The water is then directed over the gills, in the case of fish and mussels, or through the BALEEN in the mouth of whales. Cilia may assist by creating currents of water. The microscopic organisms are trapped and removed by, for example, GILL RAKERS which pass them backwards towards the gut.

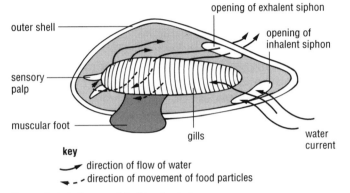

key

→ direction of flow of water
- - ► direction of movement of food particles

Figure 3.1.4 A mussel (a filter feeder)

Saprophytic organisms

Saprophytes are HETEROTROPHIC bacteria and fungi which feed on the dead remains of plants and animals. They carry out extracellular digestion by releasing enzymes onto their food and then absorbing the digested food. Saprophytes are vitally important in the recycling of nutrients (see section 6.3).

Symbiosis

This means 'living together' – two organisms of different species live together and in many cases they are unable to live separately. The closeness of the relationship varies, as does the benefit each receives. Here are some examples of symbiotic relationships:

- Lichen: this is a very close relationship between an alga and a fungus. The lichen can grow on bare surfaces such as rocks. The alga benefits because of the fungus's ability to hold water. The fungus benefits because of the alga's ability to make carbohydrate by photosynthesis.
- Bacteria living in the stomach of cows: the bacteria help to digest the cellulose, and benefit by having plenty of food available and also by being protected.
- Leguminous plants (peas and beans) have root nodules in which symbiotic bacteria live (see section 6.3); the bacteria 'fix' nitrogen for the plant and in return receive sugars produced by the plant in photosynthesis.

Parasitism

This can be thought of as a form of symbiosis. Unlike the examples mentioned above, where both species benefit, here only one benefits and the other is harmed in some way. The host may be deprived of its food or be structurally damaged, or the parasite may act as a vector of a disease-causing organism.

Some parasites live *on* the host (ECTOPARASITES); for example, greenflies (aphids) live on plants using their piercing mouthparts to reach the PHLOEM and remove the sugary solution it contains. This deprives the leaf and other parts of the plant of food and in addition the aphid may transmit diseases caused by plant viruses. Insecticides may be used to control them, those that are taken into the plant and carried in its phloem being the most useful.

Some parasites live *inside* their host (ENDOPARASITES). These often have structural adaptations and complex life-cycles involving a secondary host. The LIVER FLUKE is a good example. This parasite has sheep and cattle as its PRIMARY HOSTS. The adult has a flattened leaf-like body, and has suckers to attach itself to the cells of the liver or bile duct. It has no need for sense organs, and once attached does not need a means of locomotion.

The life-cycle involves water snails – the SECONDARY HOST. The fertilised eggs are deposited on grass along with sheep or cattle faeces. These hatch, producing larvae that infect the snail. Inside the snail there is asexual multiplication of the larvae. Each snail can release many larvae, which form cysts. If these are eaten by a sheep or cow, the cysts hatch; the larvae bore through the gut wall and migrate to the liver.

Quick Questions

1 What kind of living organisms are called autotrophs, and why?
2 Why do herbivores need specialised dentitions (teeth) and digestive systems?
3 List three differences between the dentition and jaw action of a herbivore such as a cow, and a carnivore such as a cat.
4 Give two examples of animals that are 'fluid feeders'.
5 What do 'filter feeders' feed on?
6 What structures in shellfish (mussels, for example) act as the filters?
7 What do saprophytes feed on?
8 What is extracellular digestion?
9 What does 'symbiosis' mean? Give an example of a symbiotic relationship.
10 In what ways are parasitic relationships different from other symbiotic relationships?

3.2 Patterns of support and movement

Skeletons

Multicellular organisms need a framework to support the structures/organs within their bodies.

Invertebrates

In animals with hydrostatic skeletons, the body is supported by the fluid in the cells and body cavities of the organism. Examples include the earthworm and slug.

Many invertebrates have a hard skeleton on the outside of their soft body (exoskeleton). Muscles are attached to this exoskeleton to allow locomotion. In INSECTS the exoskeleton is made of CHITIN, but in CRUSTACEANS such as crabs it is made of CALCIUM CARBONATE. Since these exoskeletons are non-living they cannot 'grow' as the animal grows, and therefore they must be cast off and replaced periodically with a new and larger one.

Vertebrates

These have an internal skeleton to which muscles are attached to allow movement and locomotion. A major factor in determining the size, mass and structure of a vertebrate's skeleton is whether the animal lives on land or in water.

Aquatic vertebrates have a similar density to that of water and therefore their body mass is supported by the water in which they live. Their skeletons do not need to be as strong as those of land vertebrates in order to support their bodies. Many of the world's largest vertebrates are aquatic, the largest being the blue whale. Their skeletons would be unable to support their body mass on land.

The shape of the skeleton in aquatic vertebrates allows them to have a body that is streamlined in outline. This reduces resistance as they move through the water.

Land vertebrates are limited in their size because their skeleton must support their total body mass. The bones must be more robust, larger and stronger than those of aquatic vertebrates, particularly the limb bones. Therefore the larger the animal, the larger and heavier is the skeleton. Because of this the larger bones are often hollow and have regions of spongy bone with air spaces. This means that the skeleton retains its strength but its mass is reduced. Birds in particular must have a very light skeleton in order to be able to fly.

Locomotion

Unicellular organisms

An *Amoeba* has the ability to change its shape. Its cytoplasm is able to flow into PSEUDOPODIA created by the cell membrane bulging out (Figure 3.2.1).

Other unicellular organisms have CILIA (as in *Paramecium*) or FLAGELLA (as in *Euglena*) (Figure 3.2.2). The cilia or flagella can beat to move the organism through the water. Their beating is coordinated, and its direction can be changed to allow changes in direction.

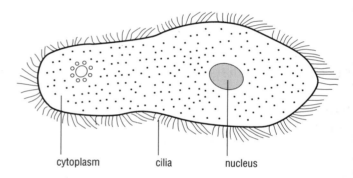

Paramecium

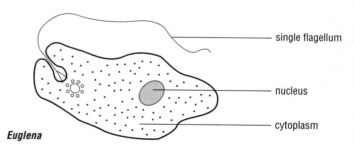

Euglena

Figure 3.2.2 Movement in ciliates and flagellates

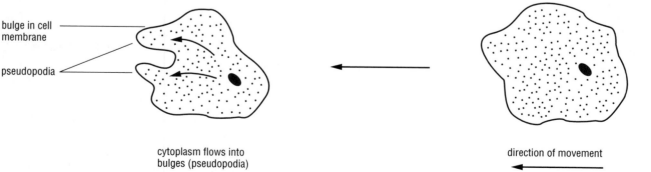

Figure 3.2.1 Movement in *Amoeba*

Multicellular organisms

Most multicellular animals have evolved specialised structures for locomotion. Although many vertebrates have evolved limbs that look very different, as in the human arm and a bird's wing, we can recognise the same plan in the arrangement of the bones. This plan is called the PENTADACTYL plan of the limb (Figure 3.2.3).

This basic plan is then modified and adapted to allow the function it must perform to take place (Figure 3.2.4). In birds and bats, for example, it forms a wing. In moles it must form a digging and tunnelling tool, and in horses the legs are designed for speed. Modification may involve fusion of bones, reduction in the size of bones or enlargement of bones. Table 3.2.1 lists some adaptations of this kind.

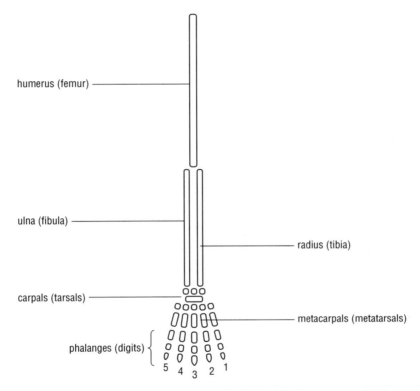

Figure 3.2.3 The pentadactyl limb (plan); the names of the bones refer to the forelimb, while the corresponding bones in the hindlimb are shown in brackets

Table 3.2.1 Modifications of the limb bones

	Bird	**Bat**	**Horse**	**Mole**
Humerus	Shortened	Thin, elongated	Shortened, thickened	Shortened, thickened
Radius	Thinner	Elongated	Fused, shortened and thickened	Shortened, thickened
Ulna	–	Thin, reduced		Elbow enlarged
Carpals	Reduced, fused	Reduced, fused	3rd metacarpal elongated, others reduced or fused	Extra bone (thumb size)
Phalanges (digits)	Reduced, fused	Elongated greatly, especially 2–5	3rd thicker, 'nail' becomes hoof	Bones are broad, so are claws
Function	Flight	Flight	Running	Digging

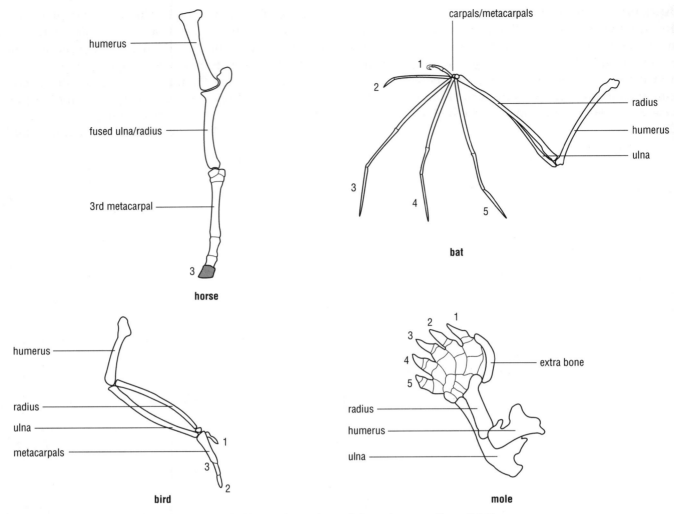

Figure 3.2.4 Modifications to the pentadactyl limb (the numbers refer to digit numbers, see Figure 3.2.3)

Locomotion in birds

Here the specialised structures are the wings. Birds' wings are shaped like aerofoils, and this allows them to generate the necessary LIFT for them to remain in the air. A bird's skeleton is very strong, but it is light because the bones have large air spaces.

As the bird glides through the air the wing is positioned so that air flows faster over the upper side of the wing than over the underside. As a result the pressure below the wing is higher than above (Figure 3.2.5). This is what creates lift.

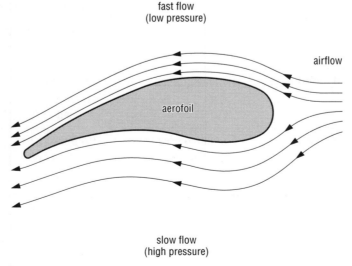

Figure 3.2.5 Air flow past a bird's wing

Flapping flight

Flight muscles, attached to the enlarged breastbone (keel) of the bird's skeleton, move the wing up (upstroke) and down (downstroke). The bones of the wing are arranged like those of the human arm; the feathers are attached to the 'forearm' (these are called 'secondary feathers') and 'hand' ('primary feathers'). The feathers have interlocking barbs and provide a large surface area. Muscles allow the wing to flex at the 'wrist'.

The downstroke

The large flight muscles contract, pulling the wing down. The wings are fully outstretched but tilted slightly forward. This gives lift and pushes the air backwards to drive the bird through the air. The pressure of the air against the feathers closes them against each other.

The upstroke

The smaller flight muscles contract, pulling the wing upwards. The wings are now tilted slightly backward. To reduce air resistance the wing is bent at the wrist and the feathers are 'open' allowing the air to flow between them.

Locomotion in fish

Fish are perfectly 'designed' for swimming:

- They have a streamlined shape to reduce water resistance.
- They have large muscle blocks on either side of the vertebral column.
- They have a large tail fin (with a large surface area) which maximises forward thrust.
- They have MEDIAN, PECTORAL and PELVIC fins which are used to stabilise their position (see Examination question 5).
- They have a SWIM BLADDER (a bag of air) which gives them buoyancy.

Swimming movements

The muscle blocks on either side of the vertebral column operate antagonistically – as the muscles on one side contract, the muscles on the other side relax. This moves the tail rapidly from side to side.

This movement of the tail causes a SIDEWAYS THRUST and also a BACKWARD THRUST. Since the sideways thrusts are equal and opposite to each other they cancel each other out, leaving only the backward thrust which moves the fish forward.

The fins of the fish provide stability and help it to steer and brake. The median fins (dorsal and ventral) prevent ROLL and YAW while the paired fins (pectoral and pelvic) prevent PITCH (Figure 3.2.6).

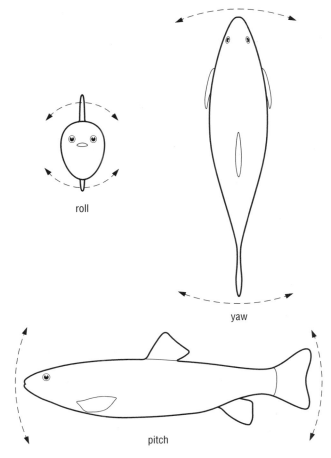

Figure 3.2.6 Types of instability in fish

roll

yaw

pitch

Quick Questions

1 What method of locomotion is used by an *Amoeba*?
2 What other method of locomotion is used by unicellular organisms?
3 What is the name given to the common plan of the arrangement of bones in the limbs of most vertebrates?
4 How is lift generated on a bird's wing as it glides through the air?
5 Give two ways in which the skeleton of a bird is adapted for flight.
6 Describe
  a) the downstroke,
  b) the upstroke,
  of a bird's wing during flapping flight.
7 How are fish adapted for swimming?
8 The muscle blocks of a fish on either side of its vertebral column work antagonistically. What does this mean?
9 How does a fish create backward thrust?
10 What is the function of:
  a) the median (dorsal and ventral) fins?
  b) the pelvic and pectoral fins?
11 What types of skeleton are found in invertebrates?
12 In what ways are the skeletons of land vertebrates different from those of aquatic vertebrates?

3.3 Patterns of reproduction

Reproduction in insects: the butterfly

Insects normally reproduce sexually and undergo METAMORPHOSIS during their life-cycle – the young stage transforms into the adult, which may be different in size, shape and behaviour.

Stages in the life-cycle of a butterfly (Figure 3.3.1)
- The male butterfly mates with the female, depositing sperm sacs in her body.
- After fertilisation the females lay large numbers of eggs, usually on a suitable food source like specific types of plant leaves.
- The eggs hatch into larvae which are commonly called CATERPILLARS. These are totally unlike the adult stage. They lack sex organs and their main function is to feed and grow.
- Eventually the larvae attach to a suitable surface by a thread of silk and then PUPATE. The pupa looks lifeless and may be protected by a cocoon of silk threads. Inside the pupa the tissues of the larva are broken down and used to form the adult – the butterfly.
- The butterfly emerges from the pupa case.

This is an example of COMPLETE METAMORPHOSIS since the appearance and the behaviour of the adult and larva are totally different.

Reproduction in amphibians: the frog

Reproduction is sexual and mating usually occurs in the spring and must occur in water. This life-cycle is another example of complete metamorphosis.

Stages in the life-cycle of the frog (Figure 3.3.2)
- During mating the male attaches itself to the female using NUPTIAL PADS (swellings on its thumbs). The male stays in position on the female's back for several days.
- As eggs leave the female's body the male releases seminal fluid containing sperm, which fertilises the eggs.
- The cluster of eggs, each surrounded by a layer of jelly (albumin for nutrition), sticks to the surface of plants or stones. This is commonly called 'frog spawn'.
- After about one week the eggs hatch into larvae, the 'tadpoles', which feed on small plants in the water.

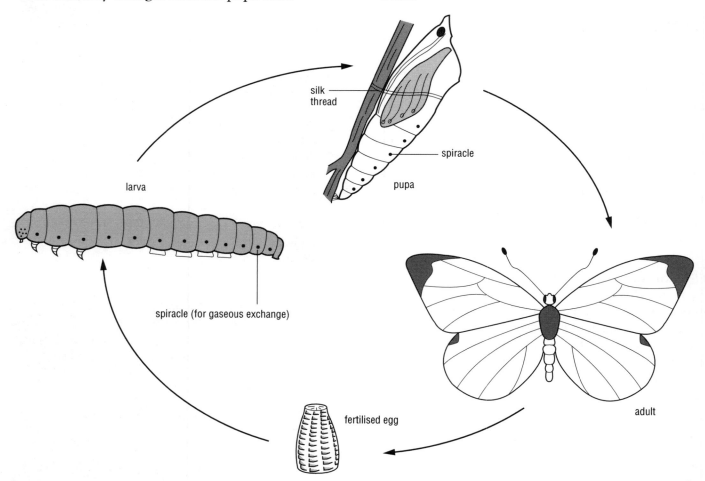

silk thread

spiracle

pupa

larva

spiracle (for gaseous exchange)

fertilised egg

adult

Figure 3.3.1 Life-cycle of a butterfly

- The tadpole undergoes a gradual transformation into a frog, which takes about 16 weeks. During this transformation the key changes are:
  a) The tadpole uses external gills for gas exchange; these are replaced by internal gills and finally lungs.

b) Hindlimbs and then forelimbs emerge from the body. These allow the tadpole to climb to the surface to breathe air.

c) The tail shortens and finally disappears.

- The young frog is able to leave the pond to feed on a variety of insects.

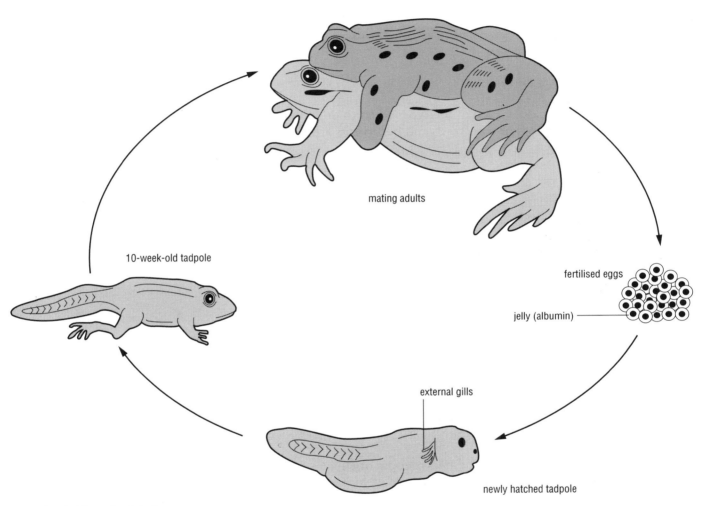

mating adults

10-week-old tadpole

fertilised eggs

jelly (albumin)

external gills

newly hatched tadpole

Figure 3.3.2 Life-cycle of the frog

Quick Questions

1. What is meant by the term 'metamorphosis' when used to describe life-cycles?
2. Where does a female butterfly usually lay her eggs, and why?
3. What do butterfly eggs hatch into?
4. What happens inside the pupa of a butterfly?
5. Where do frogs mate?
6. What is frog spawn?
7. List the major changes that occur in the development of a tadpole into a frog.

Section Three: Examination Questions

1. The drawing shows the side view of the skull of a carnivore.

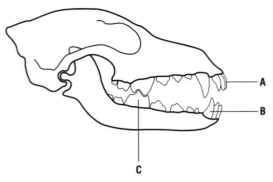

   (a) Label the teeth **A**, **B** and **C**.   [3]

   (b) What special job does each of the types of teeth do in helping this carnivore feed?   [3]

   (c) The jaw movements of carnivores and herbivores are different because they eat different kinds of food.

      (i)   Describe the jaw action of a carnivore.   [1]

      (ii) Describe the jaw action of a herbivore.   [1]

(SEG, Foundation, Specimen)

2. The drawing shows some of the parts of a mollusc which lives in seawater. It feeds on the microscopic organisms living in the water.

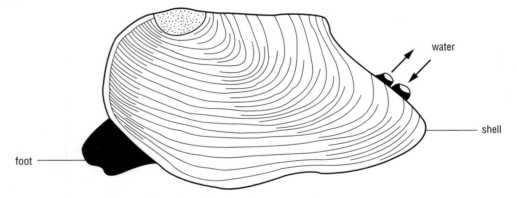

   (a) What is the name given to the microscopic organisms on which this mollusc feeds?   [1]

   (b) Describe how this mollusc feeds. Include in your answer the name of its method of feeding.   [4]

(SEG, Foundation, Specimen)

3. The drawing shows the skeleton of an extinct animal.

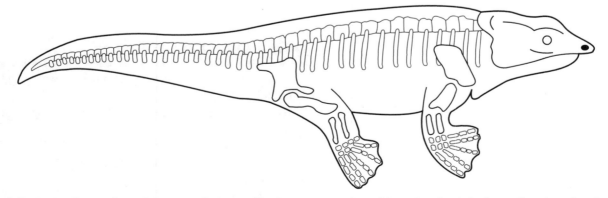

   (a) Describe and explain **one** feature which suggests that this animal might have lived on land.   [2]

   (b) Describe and explain **one** feature which suggests that this animal might have lived in water.   [2]

(SEG, Foundation, Specimen)

4. (a) The drawing shows the skeleton of a bird.

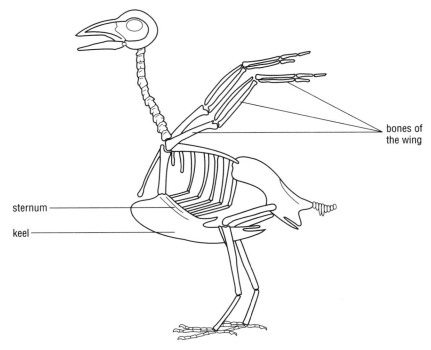

(i) Explain why the sternum and keel are large in birds. [2]

(ii) The drawing shows the structure of the inside of a wing bone of a bird. Explain why it looks like this. [2]

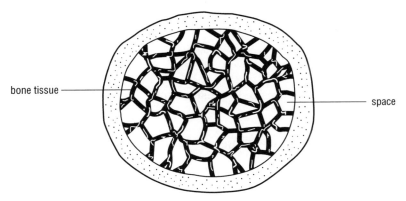

(b) The diagrams show a bird in flight.

(Source: MBV Roberts)

Use the words in the box to complete the gaps in the sentences to explain how birds fly. You may use each word once, more than once or not at all.

aerofoil	closed flat	downstroke	downwards	drag	lift	sideways	upstroke

During flight the .... is the power stroke and the wing moves .... and forwards. During this stroke the feathers are .... against each other. This allows air to rush around the wing to provide .... On the .... the feathers swivel to allow air to flow through.

[5]

(SEG, Foundation, Specimen)

5. **(a)** The drawing shows the arrangement of fins on a fish. The fins are necessary for stability as the fish moves through the water.

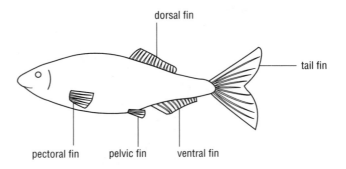

  (i)   Which fins reduce rolling?   [1]
  (ii) Which fins reduce yawing?   [1]
  (iii) Which fins reduce pitching?   [1]

  (b) The drawing shows the arrangement of the swimming muscles around the backbone of a fish.

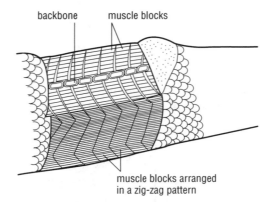

  How does the action of these muscles help a fish swim?   [4]

  (SEG, Higher, Specimen)

6. The drawing shows a liver fluke, a parasite in sheep.

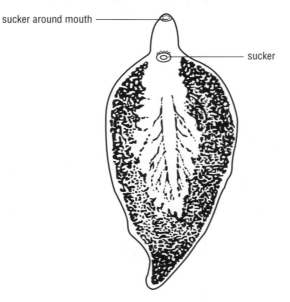

  (a) Explain the term 'parasite'.   [3]
  (b) Give **one** feature, from the drawing, which shows how the liver fluke is adapted to a parasitic way of life.   [1]

  (CCEA, Tier R, June 1996)

Section
FOUR

Green plants
as organisms

4.1 Plant nutrition

The vast majority of flowering plants have the following main regions:

- Roots, which anchor them firmly in the ground.
- Stems, to hold them upright towards the light and to transport substances between their parts.
- Leaves, used to absorb sunlight energy to enable them to make their own food.

Green plants have the ability to manufacture organic foods (like carbohydrates) from simple inorganic materials like water and carbon dioxide, using sunlight energy. Oxygen is released as a by-product. As the process involves sunlight energy it is called **photosynthesis**. Four factors must be present for photosynthesis:

- Light, absorbed by chlorophyll in CHLOROPLASTS.
- Carbon dioxide, which dissolves in the surface moisture layer of the SPONGY MESOPHYLL cells of the leaf and then diffuses into the PALISADE LAYER.
- Water.
- Chlorophyll.

The overall process can be represented in the word and chemical equations below, which show raw materials and end-products:

$$\text{carbon dioxide} + \text{water} \xrightarrow[\substack{\text{in presence of}\\\text{light and chlorophyll}}]{} \text{glucose} + \text{oxygen}$$

$$6CO_2 + 6H_2O \longrightarrow C_6H_{12}O_6 + 6O_2$$

Photosynthesis is sometimes referred to as carbon **assimilation** or carbon fixation. It occurs in the leaf and other green parts of plants where the chlorophyll is found. Chlorophyll is contained in microscopic structures called chloroplasts, which are especially numerous in the PALISADE cells of the leaf (Figure 4.1.1).

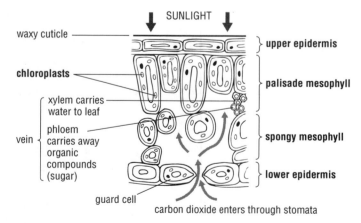

Figure 4.1.1 Section through a leaf during photosynthesis

There are no chloroplasts in the epidermis of leaves, except in the guard cells found around the stomata.

Adaptations of the leaf for photosynthesis and gaseous exchange

- Leaves are usually broad and flat; this ensures that the leaf can absorb as much light as possible.
- Leaves are usually thin (from top to bottom), which ensures that the carbon dioxide needed for photosynthesis only has to diffuse a short distance.
- The palisade cells are arranged at right angles to the epidermis to ensure the maximum number can be fitted into the space available. This arrangement also ensures that the maximum number of chloroplasts is exposed to sunlight. It also reduces absorption of light by cell walls, which would be substantial if the cells were stacked one on top of the other.
- The palisade cells contain large numbers of chloroplasts to ensure maximum absorption of light.
- There is an extensive system of interconnecting intercellular spaces in the spongy mesophyll. These are in contact with the air surrounding the leaves via the many stomata. This provides a large surface area of moist cell walls over which gaseous exchange can take place. (Remember that plants need carbon dioxide for photosynthesis and oxygen for respiration.)
- Guard cells surround each stoma. They determine the diameter of the stomata and therefore how much gas exchange takes place (see section 4.3 for details).
- There is a well-developed transport system. Xylem brings the water for photosynthesis to the palisade cells. Phloem transports the products of photosynthesis from the leaf to all plant regions.

Experiments used to investigate photosynthesis

If photosynthesis is taking place in a plant, glucose will be present in its leaves. This glucose is rapidly converted to starch. Therefore we can test leaves for the presence of glucose or starch to find out if photosynthesis is taking place.

Leaves can be crushed and tested with Benedict's reagent to test for the presence of glucose. Testing leaves for starch is more common.

Testing leaves for the presence of starch
1 The leaf is placed in boiling water for one minute. This kills cells and makes the cell membranes permeable to iodine solution and chlorophyll.
2 The leaf is placed in boiling alcohol in a hot-water-bath (above 77 °C, but with the Bunsen burner *turned off*). This removes the chlorophyll from the leaf cells as it is soluble in the hot alcohol.

3 The leaf is washed gently in water to soften the cells as they become dehydrated in the alcohol. The water also removes excess alcohol from the leaf surface.

4 Iodine solution is dropped on to the leaf. A blue/black colour indicates the presence of starch.

Destarching plants

It is necessary to remove all starch from a plant if we are investigating photosynthesis. This is because we are using the presence of starch as evidence that the process has taken place. Destarching a plant is achieved simply by keeping it in complete darkness for 24–36 hours.

Investigating the need for light

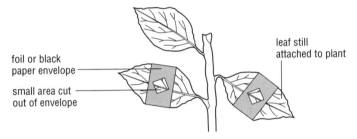

Figure 4.1.2 The need for light in photosynthesis

A destarched plant is set up as shown in Figure 4.1.2, and its leaves are tested for starch after 24 hours exposure to light (Figure 4.1.3).

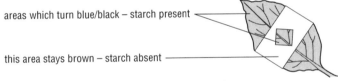

Figure 4.1.3 A leaf after being tested for starch

Clearly light is needed for the process of photosynthesis, since starch is not made in its absence.

Investigating the need for carbon dioxide

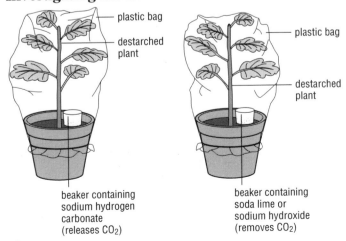

Figure 4.1.4 The need for carbon dioxide in photosynthesis

A destarched plant is set up as in Figure 4.1.4 and its leaves tested for starch after 24 hours.

The leaves exposed to soda lime/sodium hydroxide do not contain starch, but those exposed to sodium hydrogen carbonate do. Therefore carbon dioxide is needed for photosynthesis.

Investigating the need for chlorophyll

Destarched plants are not needed; variegated plants are used instead, because these have chlorophyll only in the green parts of their leaves (Figure 4.1.5). There are many types of variegated plants, including certain species of ivy and pelargonium.

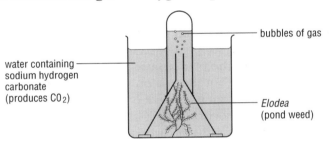

Figure 4.1.5 The need for chlorophyll in photosynthesis

Demonstrating that oxygen is produced

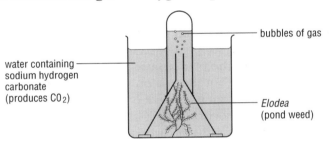

Figure 4.1.6 Oxygen production in photosynthesis

A sprig of *Elodea* is set up under water as shown in Figure 4.1.6. If the gas collected is tested with a glowing splint it relights, proving that it must be oxygen.

Factors affecting the rate of photosynthesis

Four factors have an effect: light, carbon dioxide, temperature and water. These factors can be investigated using pond weed (*Elodea*) and its rate of oxygen production.

- Light: up to an optimum light intensity, the brighter the light the higher is the rate of photosynthesis. Therefore to promote rapid photosynthesis, and therefore growth and yield, growers plant crops in sunny areas and in glasshouses where artificial light is used to optimise light levels. It is not just the intensity of light that is important, however, it is also its wavelength. Green plants reflect 'green' light and absorb blue and red light best. Therefore the rate of photosynthesis would be lowest in green light and highest in red and blue light.

- Carbon dioxide: increased levels of carbon dioxide increase the rate of photosynthesis. The amount of carbon dioxide in the atmosphere is about 0.03%, and this does not vary much except close to the ground in a dense forest. Carbon dioxide is sometimes pumped into greenhouses, however. More usually growers use propane or butane burners, which produce carbon dioxide and therefore increase yield.
- Temperature: up to an optimum temperature, the higher the temperature the faster the plant will photosynthesise. A rise of 10 °C doubles the rate. Plants will therefore grow faster in a greenhouse. The maximum temperature is about 40 °C; above this photosynthesis will slow as enzymes become affected/denatured.
- Water: this is needed for photosynthesis and normally most plants have a sufficient supply. A plant beginning to wilt through lack of water closes its stomata, thus reducing uptake of carbon dioxide and slowing down photosynthesis.

Limiting factors

The rate of photosynthesis is controlled by the availability of several factors. At any particular time the rate of photosynthesis is determined by the factor that is in shortest supply. For example, if there is enough light for the plant to use 5 mg of carbon dioxide per hour but there is only 1 mg of carbon dioxide available, then the lack of carbon dioxide is preventing the process from speeding up. Only an increase in the amount of carbon dioxide could speed up the process in these circumstances.

At the beginning and end of a day, when light is dim, light is likely to be the limiting factor. At midday, when light is at its brightest, carbon dioxide is more likely to be limiting.

Limiting factors are especially important in artificial systems like glasshouses. Growers must try to produce optimum conditions for photosynthesis.

After photosynthesis

The glucose molecules may be:

- Used in respiration to release energy for metabolic processes in the leaf cells.
- Joined together to form larger molecules such as starch. These can be stored and used during darkness to provide energy in respiration as no photosynthesis can occur.
- Used for the formation of new cell walls. Here the glucose molecules are linked together to form long chains of cellulose.
- Built up into proteins using the nitrates and other nutrients in the water brought up to the leaves in the xylem.

- Transported away from the leaf through the phloem as sucrose to other parts of the plant where it is needed for growth – of root and shoot tips, for example.
- Converted into food stores for seeds (for example, as lipid and starch), fruits (as sucrose) or underground storage organs (as starch). It is an advantage to a plant to store carbohydrate as starch rather than sugars. This is partly because the starch molecule is very compact, but more importantly it is because starch is insoluble and therefore does not cause large amounts of water to accumulate in storage cells as a result of osmosis (Figure 4.1.7).

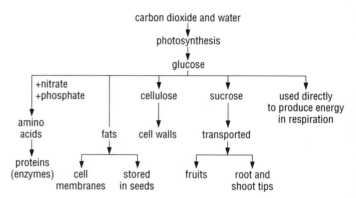

Figure 4.1.7 What happens to glucose in the plant

Comparing respiration and photosynthesis

Remember that plant cells respire *all* the time, and that photosynthesis can only take place when there is sufficient light. Therefore during daylight both processes will occur. The glucose and oxygen produced by photosynthesis can be used by the plant for respiration. The carbon dioxide and water produced in respiration can be used for photosynthesis. Under certain conditions the two processes are in perfect balance, that is, at the **compensation point**. At this point there is no increase or decrease in dry matter. This means that they produce glucose in photosynthesis as fast as they use it in respiration (Figure 4.1.8).

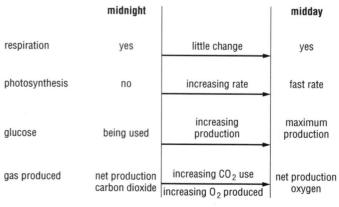

	midnight		midday
respiration	yes	little change	yes
photosynthesis	no	increasing rate	fast rate
glucose	being used	increasing production	maximum production
gas produced	net production carbon dioxide	increasing CO₂ use / increasing O₂ produced	net production oxygen

Figure 4.1.8 Respiration and photosynthesis through the day

The role of mineral ions in plant growth

Plants require many minerals (nutrients) from the soil but the following are of especial importance:

- Nitrogen, taken in as NITRATE IONS. These provide the nitrogen for the synthesis of protein from simple carbohydrate. Lack of nitrate leads to stunted growth and yellowing of older leaves.
- Potassium, needed for the proper functioning of the enzymes involved in photosynthesis and respiration, and also for bud formation and flowering. Lack of potassium leads to yellowing of leaves with dead spots.
- Phosphate, which is essential for the reactions involved in photosynthesis and respiration. Lack of phosphate results in poor root growth and purple younger leaves.
- Magnesium, needed for production of chlorophyll. Lack of magnesium causes yellowing of leaves and a slowing of growth.
- Calcium, needed for production of cell walls. Lack of calcium leads to poor development of leaf buds and stunted growth.

Investigating plant mineral requirements

This is usually done using water culture experiments. Seedlings are grown in culture solutions containing precise combinations of a range of mineral ions. One seedling is grown in a 'complete culture solution', which contains all minerals required (Figure 4.1.9). Others are grown in culture solutions each of which lacks one mineral ion. Growth of their shoots, roots and leaves is observed to identify the effect of mineral-ion deficiency.

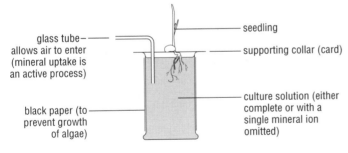

glass tube– allows air to enter (mineral uptake is an active process)

seedling

supporting collar (card)

black paper (to prevent growth of algae)

culture solution (either complete or with a single mineral ion omitted)

Figure 4.1.9 Investigating plant mineral requirements

Fertilisers

Some farmers repeatedly use the same fields for the growing of crops. They harvest the crops every year, so preventing cycling of minerals (nutrients) (see section 6.2). This is why they need to use fertilisers to ensure that there are good crop yields.

Organic fertilisers include farmyard manure (animal faeces), compost (rotting vegetable matter) and green manure (green plants specially grown and then ploughed into the soil).

Inorganic fertilisers are now being used more and more instead. The ones most commonly used contain nitrogen, phosphorus and potassium (as nitrates and ammonium salts). These are manufactured by chemical processes like the Haber process.

Fertilisers must be applied in a form that is easily absorbed by the plants. They can be applied in pellet form, or sprayed in liquid form on to the soil. They must not be too concentrated, otherwise water will leave the roots by osmosis and the plants will wilt.

Positive and negative effects of the use of inorganic fertilisers

Positive:

- They greatly increase the yield of crop plants. More food can be produced more cheaply.
- Plants can be grown more closely together so that more can be grown per unit area, again increasing productivity.
- Less land needs to be used for growing crops because productivity is so high in cultivated areas.

Negative:

- Excess runs off into rivers and lakes, causing eutrophication (see section 6.2 for details).
- Nitrates can build up in drinking water. In young children this can lead to shortage of oxygen in the tissues (the nitrate reduces the amount of oxygen carried in the blood). It has also been linked to stomach cancer.

Quick Questions

1 What are the word and chemical equations for photosynthesis?
2 What four factors are needed for photosynthesis?
3 Where exactly does photosynthesis take place in plants?
4 In what ways are leaves adapted for efficient photosynthesis and gaseous exchange?
5 What effect do light, carbon dioxide and temperature have on the rate of photosynthesis?
6 What do we call the external factor/condition that determines the overall rate of photosynthesis?
7 How can owners of glasshouses increase their crop yield?
8 Why are the following needed in green plants?
 a) Nitrogen;
 b) Potassium;
 c) Phosphate;
 d) Magnesium;
 e) Calcium.
9 Explain why plants do not appear to release carbon dioxide at midday, whereas at midnight the only gas given off is carbon dioxide.
10 What are the positive and negative effects of using inorganic fertilisers?

4.2 Plant hormones (plant growth substances)

Plants are sensitive to their environment and are capable of responding to it. It is possible to show that the growth of plants and their response to stimuli is under the control of plant growth substances (hormones). Plants are sensitive to light, gravity and moisture.

It is possible to demonstrate that the tip of a plant shoot produces a substance which is transported down the shoot and affects growth. This substance is called **auxin**. The demonstrations are shown in Figures 4.2.1, 4.2.2 and 4.2.3.

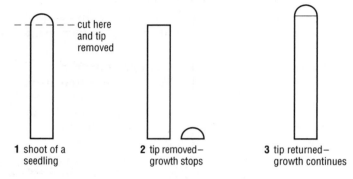

1 shoot of a seedling
2 tip removed – growth stops
3 tip returned – growth continues

Figure 4.2.1 Experiment to find out if a shoot tip influences growth

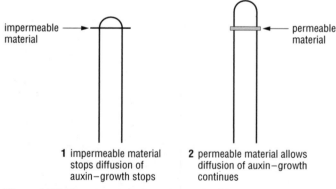

impermeable material
permeable material

1 impermeable material stops diffusion of auxin – growth stops
2 permeable material allows diffusion of auxin – growth continues

Figure 4.2.2 Experiment to show that auxin diffuses from the shoot tip

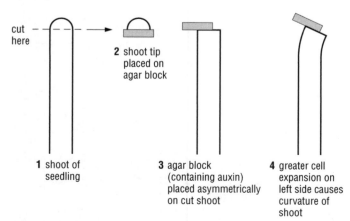

cut here

2 shoot tip placed on agar block

1 shoot of seedling
3 agar block (containing auxin) placed asymmetrically on cut shoot
4 greater cell expansion on left side causes curvature of shoot

Figure 4.2.3 Experiment to show that auxin can cause growth curvature

Auxin is a plant hormone produced by the tip of a shoot. It slowly diffuses downwards affecting growth. Auxin affects plant cell growth by controlling cell elongation/expansion. The effect of auxin on cell expansion depends on its concentration. Auxin does not promote growth in all plant cells, in fact in root cells it has the opposite effect (see 'Geotropism', opposite).

Auxin inhibits the development of side-branches. If a shoot tip (and therefore auxin) is removed, many side-branches will develop. This explains why pruning trees makes them produce lots of side-branches and makes them more 'bushy'.

Tropisms

Tropisms are the growth responses of plants towards or away from a stimulus. These responses are slow but long-lasting. Plants respond to light, gravity and water.

Phototropism

This is a plant growth response to light. Plant shoots will grow towards the light, ensuring they have sufficient light for photosynthesis. A plant shoot is said to be POSITIVELY PHOTOTROPIC. Roots on the other hand are NEGATIVELY PHOTOTROPIC, that is, they grow away from light. It is possible to demonstrate the response of seedlings to light using a tropism box (Figure 4.2.4):

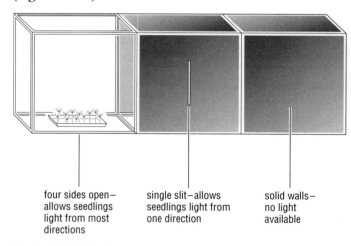

four sides open – allows seedlings light from most directions
single slit – allows seedlings light from one direction
solid walls – no light available

Figure 4.2.4 A tropism box

- The seedlings exposed to light from all directions show a normal growth pattern.
- The seedlings exposed to light from only one direction will grow towards the light source.
- Seedlings in total darkness will grow very tall and spindly with small pale green or yellow leaves. The plants are said to be **etiolated**.

Figure 4.2.5 illustrates an experiment to show that it is the shoot tip that is sensitive to light. The seedling that has its tip covered (**a**) does not grow towards the light. The seedling with its tip exposed to light (**b**) does grow towards the light.

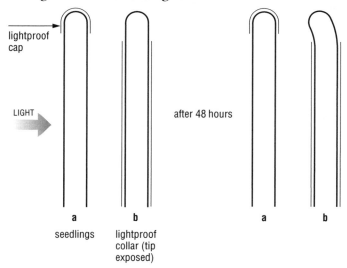

Figure 4.2.5 Investigating the sensitivity of a shoot tip to light

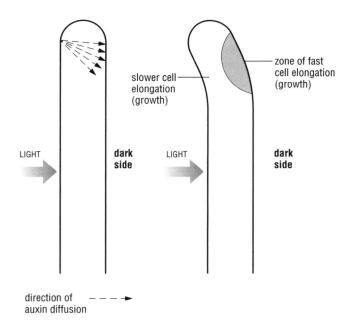

Figure 4.2.6 A shoot tip grows towards the light

When exposed to light from one direction only auxin tends to diffuse away from the light, accumulating on the 'dark' side of the shoot. This causes faster growth on one side – the 'dark' side – because of greater cell elongation. This makes the shoot bend towards the light (Figure 4.2.6).

Geotropism
Growth responses to gravity are called geotropisms. Roots are POSITIVELY GEOTROPIC, which means they grow in the same direction that gravity acts. Shoots are NEGATIVELY GEOTROPIC, which means they grow in the opposite direction from gravity.

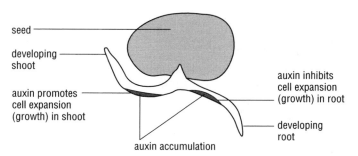

Figure 4.2.7 Geotropic responses of a root and shoot

Auxin accumulates on the lower side of a developing shoot and root (Figure 4.2.7). It inhibits cell expansion of the root cells but promotes cell expansion of the shoot cells. This causes curvature upwards in the shoot and downwards in the root.

Hydrotropism
This is a plant's growth response to water. Plant roots are POSITIVELY HYDROTROPIC. Oak and willow roots are notorious for their ability to locate and grow towards sources of water, and they are often responsible for damage to buildings and drains as a result.

Uses of plant growth substances (hormones)
Plant hormones are used commercially in agriculture and in horticulture:

- Rooting powder (auxin) is sold commercially to encourage root growth in plant cuttings. This means large numbers of plants can be produced quickly.
- They are used by fruit growers to encourage fruit development and prevent fruit fall.
- They are used to regulate the time of ripening of fruit. This allows fruit to be harvested and transported more easily.
- They can be sprayed on plants to make them develop fruits without their flowers having been fertilised.
- They can be used in agriculture as weedkillers. They disrupt normal growth patterns, speeding up the rate of respiration.

Quick Questions
1 To what three stimuli are plants sensitive?
2 What is the name of the hormone (growth substance) produced by the shoot tip?
3 How does this substance affect the growth of plant cells?
4 What are tropisms?
5 Explain why a plant shoot grows towards light.
6 Roots are 'positively geotropic'. What does this mean?
7 List the ways in which plant hormones are used commercially.

4.3 Transport and water relations

Uptake of water in roots

Roots take up water from the surrounding soil water. The concentration of solute molecules inside the root hair cells is greater than that in the soil water. Therefore the concentration of water molecules is greater outside than inside. As a result water will enter the root hair cells by osmosis. If the roots are surrounded by salt water then water may leave the roots by osmosis, thus causing wilting.

Water passes from one cell to the next by osmosis until it reaches the xylem vessels. These are very narrow tubes which carry water and dissolved mineral ions through the root, stem and leaf.

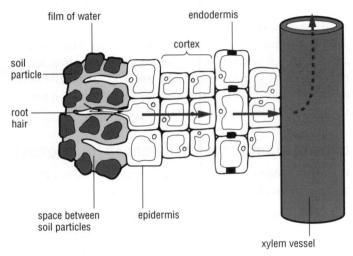

Figure 4.3.1 The passage of water into a root

Transpiration

The loss of water from the shoot system of a plant is known as **transpiration**. This involves the evaporation of water from the moist cell walls of the spongy mesophyll layer in the leaves. The water vapour produced builds up in the air spaces between the cells and is then lost by diffusion through the stomata of the leaves. This can be a huge disadvantage to plants in terms of water loss, but they must have the stomata to allow gaseous exchange to take place at the moist mesophyll cells.

Loss of water from the mesophyll cells causes water to be drawn from adjacent cells and eventually from the XYLEM VESSELS of the leaf, which in turn pulls water out of the xylem vessels in the stem and then from the root. This 'column' of water in the plant from leaf to root is known as the TRANSPIRATION STREAM. It is important to remember that it is the loss of water from the leaves by evaporation which causes the uptake and ascent of water in a fully 'leaved' plant; it is called TRANSPIRATION PULL.

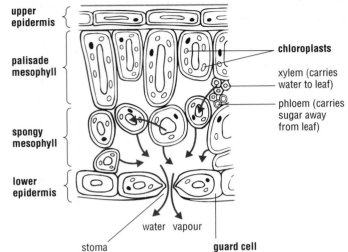

Figure 4.3.2 Water movement in a leaf

Clearly the leaf is adapted for efficient gas exchange and therefore transpiration is inevitable (see section 4.1).

Control of the size of the stomata

The size of the opening of each stoma is controlled by the guard cells which surround it. The shape of the guard cells depends on how much water they contain, whether they are turgid or flaccid. If the guard cells are turgid the stoma is wide open, and if they are flaccid it is closed. Thus the size of the stomata is controlled by the movement of water into and out of the guard cells by osmosis.

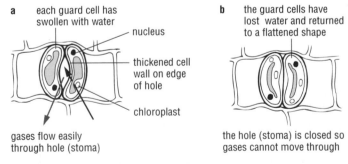

Figure 4.3.3 How stomata open and close in a leaf: (**a**) in the daytime, (**b**) at night

The potometer

This is used to measure WATER UPTAKE, and so to compare rates of transpiration between different species of plant. Remember that it does not measure the rate of water loss, only water uptake.

We can compare transpiration rates by measuring the rate at which the air bubble moves along the capillary tube under different conditions (for example, light or dark, windy or still).

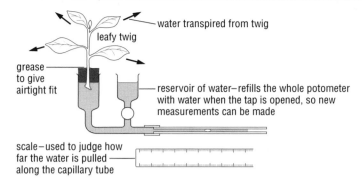

water transpired from twig

leafy twig

grease to give airtight fit

reservoir of water–refills the whole potometer with water when the tap is opened, so new measurements can be made

scale–used to judge how far the water is pulled along the capillary tube

Figure 4.3.4 How a potometer works

Factors affecting the rate of transpiration

- Humidity: transpiration will only take place if the concentration of water vapour inside the leaf is higher than outside the leaf – movement is from a high concentration to a lower concentration.
- Temperature: warm air can take up and hold more water than cool air. Its molecules also move faster. So, the higher the temperature, the faster the rate of transpiration as molecules diffuse more quickly.
- Air movement or wind: in still air, the air surrounding the leaf quickly becomes saturated with water vapour and therefore the rate of transpiration will slow down as the concentration gradient becomes less steep. In windy conditions the humid air around a leaf is dispersed thus speeding up transpiration.
- Time of day: stomata are open during daylight hours, and because of this more water vapour is lost through them.
- High altitude: this can also speed up the process as at lower air pressure there is less resistance to the movement of water molecules as they escape through the stomata.

Factors that may reduce water loss in plants

- Most plants have a waxy cuticle on their leaves which stops them from losing too much water. Plants living in drier conditions have a thicker cuticle.
- The leaves may be rolled up to reduce air movement around the stomata.
- In some plants the stomata are sunk in 'pits' in the surface of the leaves.
- The leaf surface may also be covered in hairs to reduce air movement.
- Reducing the leaf surface area lowers the number of stomata. Cacti represent the extreme case where the leaves have been lost altogether and all that is left is a photosynthetic stem. The disadvantage in reducing the leaf area is a lower rate of photosynthesis and therefore a lower rate of growth. This is because the plants have a smaller surface area for absorbing light and diffusion of carbon dioxide is slower.

Water uptake and support in plants

When plant cells are full of water they are said to be turgid (see section 1.2). Turgid cells provide support for the plant and help maintain shape. If a plant is losing water faster than it can be replaced by the roots, its cells will become plasmolysed and it will wilt. As wilting occurs the guard cells lose their water, change shape and close the stomata. This reduces transpiration.

Uptake of minerals

Minerals are taken in by the root hair cells. It is thought that the mineral ions enter the cell by diffusion, from a region of high concentration to a region of low concentration.

Ions can still enter, however, even if their concentration is lower inside the root. This uptake must therefore be by active transport (movement against the concentration gradient). Once inside the root the ions are taken in solution to the xylem vessels and then up to the leaves in the transpiration stream. They can also be moved laterally into the phloem from the xylem.

Transport of food

Running parallel with xylem vessels are phloem vessels. These carry nutrients such as sugars from the leaves to the rest of the plant, including the growing regions and the storage organs.

Quick Questions

1. How is water taken up by root hair cells?
2. What would be the effect of salt water on the movement of water into and out of roots? Explain.
3. Name the plant tissue through which water is transported.
4. What is transpiration?
5. Why is transpiration from leaves inevitable?
6. How is the size of the stomata controlled?
7. List the factors that affect the rate of transpiration.
8. What apparatus is used to compare the rates of transpiration?
9. List the features plants can develop to enable them to reduce their rate of water loss.
10. What has happened to the cells of a plant if the plant has wilted?
11. How are mineral ions taken up by plant roots?
12. Name the plant tissue through which food molecules are transported.

4.4 Plant reproduction

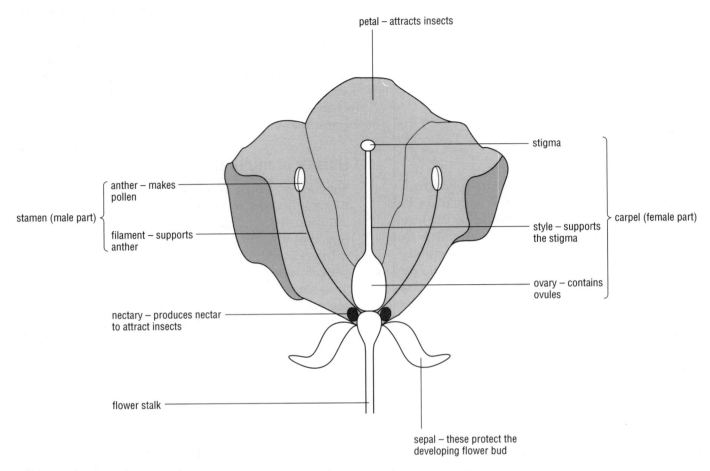

petal – attracts insects

stigma

anther – makes pollen

stamen (male part)

filament – supports anther

style – supports the stigma

carpel (female part)

ovary – contains ovules

nectary – produces nectar to attract insects

flower stalk

sepal – these protect the developing flower bud

Figure 4.4.1 Section through a flower

Flower structure

All flowers have the basic structure shown in Figure 4.4.1. These structures differ in shape and size between different species and also between insect- and wind-pollinated flowers.

Flower function

This is to produce gametes and to ensure that fertilisation occurs. To achieve this flowers must ensure that **pollination** takes place. Pollination is the transfer of pollen (which contains the male nucleus) from the anther of the stamen to the stigma of the carpel.

Some plants, such as lettuce, carry out SELF-POLLINATION. Here pollen is transferred from anther to stigma within the same flower or to another flower on the same plant. Other plants, like wallflowers, carry out CROSS-POLLINATION. This is the transfer of pollen from the anther to the stigma of a flower on a different plant of the same species.

Pollen is transferred either by insects or by the wind, and plants show distinct structural adaptations depending on which method they use (Table 4.4.1).

Table 4.4.1 Adaptations for pollination

Insect-pollinated flowers	Wind-pollinated flowers
Petals brightly coloured and large	Petals much smaller and green or dull
Nectar secreted by nectaries at base of petals	No nectaries present
Stamens are short and found inside the flower	Stamens are long, hanging out of the flower, and are easily shaken
Stigma is short and found inside the flower	Stigma is feathery, giving it a large surface area, and hangs outside the flower
Pollen grains may be spiky or sticky	Larger numbers of pollen grains produced; grains are very light and may have air sacs

The features of an insect-pollinated flower attract insects to them. This makes the successful transfer of the pollen between flowers more likely, as the insects will visit many plants in search of nectar. Similarly, the characteristics of wind-pollinated plants ensure that pollen is scattered over a wide area and again increases the chances of pollination.

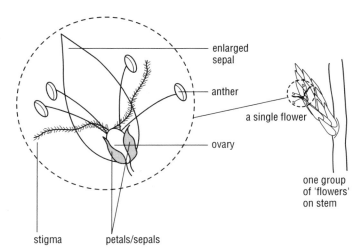

Figure 4.4.2 Flower of a glass plant (wind-pollinated)

Fertilisation

After pollination has occurred the pollen grain develops and grows a tube-like structure. This grows into the tissues of the stigma and style, using sugars and other materials in the style for nourishment. Eventually the pollen tube reaches the ovule in the ovary and penetrates the micropyle (a tiny opening in the surface of the ovule) (Figure 4.4.3). Once inside this structure the tip of the pollen tube bursts open and releases the male nucleus. This then fuses with the female nucleus of the egg cell. Fertilisation is complete.

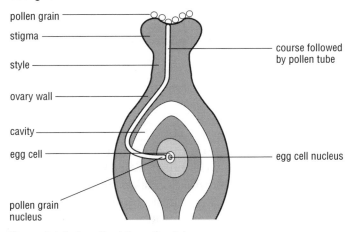

Figure 4.4.3 Growth of the pollen tube

Seed structure

The fertilised egg cell divides by mitosis to form a ball of cells known as the EMBRYO. This eventually develops a tiny root (the RADICLE), a tiny shoot (the PLUMULE) and a pair of seed leaves (the COTYLEDONS). These are often thicker than normal leaves as they sometimes contain a food store.

The embryo becomes surrounded by a food store called the ENDOSPERM. The ovule eventually forms the seed (Figure 4.4.4), the wall of which is the TESTA. The testa becomes very hard and is resistant to fungal and

bacterial attack. The old ovary wall will develop into the fruit around the ovule or seed. In the last stage of seed formation, water is withdrawn to enable it to survive harsh conditions like cold or drought.

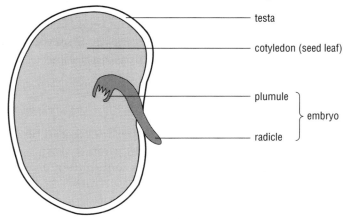

Figure 4.4.4 Section through a seed

Fruit and seed dispersal

(Do not confuse this with pollen dispersal.)
Dispersal is essential to keep down overcrowding and therefore competition between young plants as they germinate and grow. It also allows a species to colonise new areas.

Types of dispersal

The mechanisms involved depend on the species and therefore the types of seed or fruit produced. There are four main mechanisms (Figure 4.4.5).

Animal dispersal
The fruit is eaten or carried by an animal, and the seeds are therefore deposited some distance away from the other seeds and also from the parent plant. Examples include fleshy fruits like holly berries, tomatoes and plums. These are often brightly coloured, and the flesh tastes good and is a useful source of energy for the animals. The seeds are often eaten with the flesh of the fruit, swallowed and passed out with the faeces, having passed through the digestive system intact. The decomposing faecal matter often provides a useful source of fertiliser.

Some dry fruits like acorns and beech nuts are gathered by squirrels for food and transported some distance away from the parent plant, many being lost by the animal on route to its 'home'.

Other fruits have hooks which attach to the fur of passing animals. An example of this type is burdock.

Wind dispersal
The fruit wall develops an outgrowth to increase surface area. This allows it to be caught more easily by air currents. These fruits are usually very light and are never succulent (fleshy). Examples include dandelion and sycamore.

Explosive dispersal

These seeds develop inside a fruit which is commonly called a 'pod'. Here the fruit wall dries out and eventually splits along a line of weakness which holds the two halves of the pod together. This splitting can be quite violent and the seeds inside can be thrown a considerable distance away from the parent plant. Examples include peas, lupins and pansies.

Water dispersal

The best example is that of the coconut which demonstrates how much larger these seeds can be compared to those carried on air currents. Most waterborne seeds have air spaces within them to enable them to float more easily.

a Animal dispersal

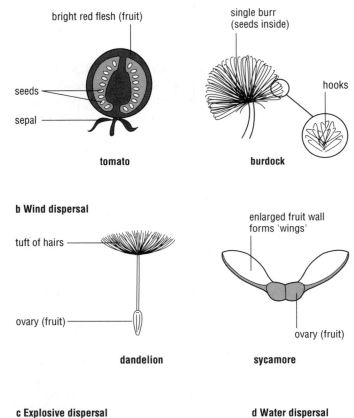

b Wind dispersal

c Explosive dispersal

d Water dispersal

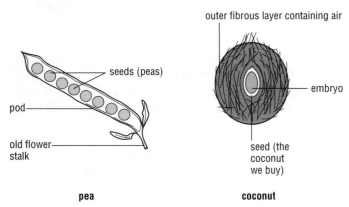

Figure 4.4.5 Methods of seed dispersal

Germination

Having been dispersed, a seed will not germinate until it has the correct conditions. These conditions will not trigger germination until a period of **dormancy** has passed. Dormancy ensures that seeds can survive harsh environmental conditions. Many seeds have to have a period of cold conditions before dormancy is broken.

During germination food reserves have to be mobilised and for this enzyme action is needed. Therefore the conditions needed for germination are those under which enzymes function normally. Provided that water is present, that the temperature is above a certain minimum, and that oxygen is available, germination will commence.

To determine the conditions necessary for germination

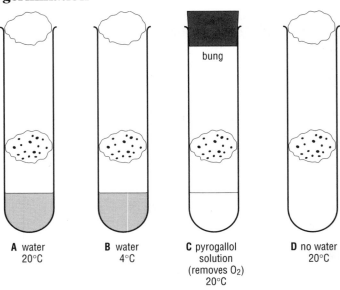

Figure 4.4.6 Investigating the conditions necessary for germination

Tube **A**: Soaked seeds on moist cotton wool, kept at 20 °C, loose cotton wool bung. Water, warmth and oxygen present – germination takes place.
Tube **B**: Soaked seeds on moist cotton wool, kept at 4 °C (refrigerator), loose cotton wool bung. Water and oxygen present – no germination.
Tube **C**: Soaked seeds on moist cotton wool, kept at 20 °C. Tight bung and no oxygen present. Water and warmth present – no germination.
Tube **D**: Dry seeds on dry cotton wool, kept at 20 °C, loose cotton wool bung. Warmth and oxygen present – no germination.

Tube **A** acts as a control. Germination will only occur in this flask.

Germination is illustrated in Figure 4.4.7. This is an example of HYPOGEAL germination. This means that the seed leaves (cotyledons) remain inside the seed case below ground.

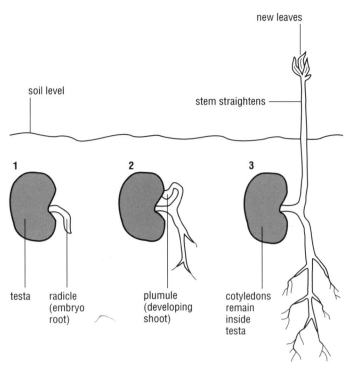

Figure 4.4.7 Germination of a seed

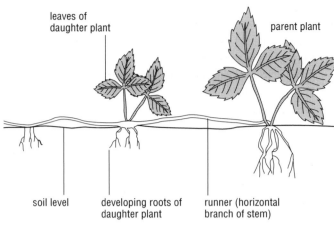

Figure 4.4.8 Strawberry runner

Propagation

Vegetative propagation is a method of asexual reproduction and therefore does not involve gametes and fertilisation. It is carried out by many species of plants and includes the formation of runners (stolons) and underground storage organs like tubers, bulbs and corms.

The creeping buttercup and the strawberry are examples of plants that can reproduce vegetatively using stolons (runners). The stolons grow horizontally from lateral buds after the stem has produced flowers. At the tip of each stolon is a bud which can produce roots as well as leaves. The stolons have long INTERNODES (distance between leaves) and have small scale-like leaves along the length of the shoot. When the apical bud (bud at the stem tip) of the stolon touches the soil it produces leaves and roots, forming a daughter plant (Figure 4.4.8). Each daughter plant will be fed by the original plant until it can live independently. The old stolon connecting the two plants will eventually dry up and wither away. All daughter plants produced in this way will be genetically identical.

Cuttings

This is an artificial method of vegetative propagation. Lengths of stem (stem cuttings) are usually taken at certain times of the year and from certain parts of the plant. If placed in water or pushed into damp soil, roots may develop at the cut surface and the shoot continues to grow as normal. Rooting powder containing a plant growth regulator (auxin) may be applied to the cut surface to encourage growth of new roots. Transpiration may be reduced by placing a clear plastic bag over the shoot system until roots have developed.

Many plants can be propagated in this way, including rhododendron, carnations and chrysanthemums.

Quick Questions

1 What are the functions of the following flower parts?
   a) Petal;
   b) Anther;
   c) Ovary;
   d) Nectary.
2 What is pollination?
3 List the differences between wind- and insect-pollinated flowers.
4 What happens to a pollen grain when it lands on the stigma of a flower?
5 Name the following parts of a seed:
   a) The embryo root;
   b) The embryo shoot;
   c) The food store.
6 List the four methods of fruit dispersal, giving an example of each.
7 What factors are needed for germination to be able to proceed in seeds?
8 What is meant by vegetative propagation?
9 How do strawberries and buttercups propagate?
10 How can we propagate plants artificially?

Section Four: Examination Questions

1. A green plant was placed in a dark cupboard. After 24 hours, some of the leaves were tested for starch. No starch was found in any leaf. The same plant was then placed in sunlight. One leaf, **Q**, was treated as shown in the diagram below. After a further 24 hours, leaves **P** and **Q** on the plant were tested for starch.

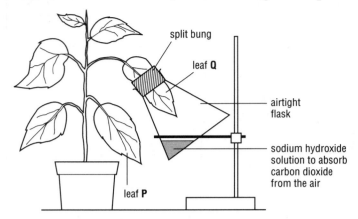

   (a) Why was there no starch in the leaves after the plant had been kept in the dark cupboard for 24 hours? [2]
   (b) (i) Name the substance in green leaves which helps plants to make glucose. [1]
   (ii) Name the gas produced by green leaves when they make glucose for starch production. [1]
   (c) The diagrams below show the results of starch tests on discs taken from leaves **P** and **Q**. The diagrams also show the parts of the leaves from which the discs were taken.

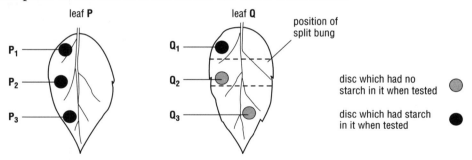

   Explain the reasons for the differences between discs P_3 and Q_3 and between discs P_2 and Q_2. [3]
   (London, Higher, Specimen)

2. The diagram shows four oat seedlings which have been set up to investigate their response to light coming from one side.

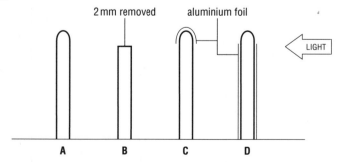

   (a) How would you arrange for the seedlings to receive light from one side only? [2]
   (b) The seedlings were left for several days with light coming from the side as shown in the diagram.
   (i) Describe what would have happened to the height of each of these seedlings. [2]
   (ii) Describe the direction of the growth movement of each seedling after this time. [4]
   (c) Which part of the oat seedling detects the direction from which the light is shining? [1]
   (d) (i) What is the name given to the growth movement of plants in response to light? [2]
   (ii) Explain how this growth response in the shoots is caused. [5]
   (SEG, Higher, Specimen)

3. The diagrams show the effects of growing Busy Lizzie plants in solutions which lack certain nutrients.

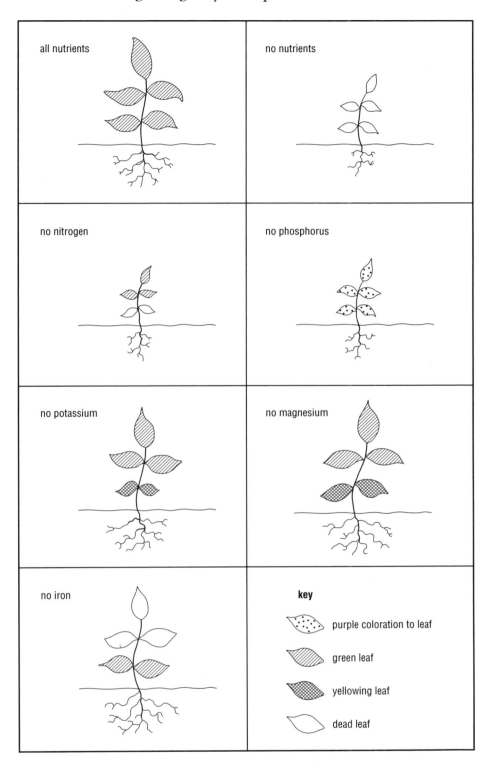

(a) What is the effect of growing Busy Lizzie plants:
   (i) Without phosphorus?
   (ii) Without iron? [4]
(b) Explain why each of the following affects the growth of Busy Lizzie plants:
   (i) No nitrogen.
   (ii) No magnesium. [3]

(NEAB, Higher, June 1994)

4. Many people like to keep pot plants inside their houses. These plants need watering regularly.
   (a) Draw arrows on the diagram to show the path taken by the water from the time it enters the plant to the time it leaves as water vapour.   [1]

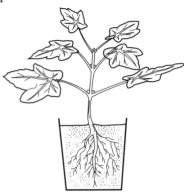

   (b) (i)   Name the process by which the water enters the plant from the soil.   [1]
       (ii) Explain how this process works.   [2]
   (c) (i)   Explain briefly how a plant loses water and how it controls the rate of loss.   [2]
       (ii) Suggest **two** reasons why it is important for a plant to be able to control its rate of water loss.   [2]

                                                                                (MEG, Higher, Specimen)

5. (a) (i)   What normally keeps the leaves of a plant firm and outstretched?   [3]
       (ii) What happens in the leaves to make them wilt?   [2]
   (b) In an investigation, the plants living in a marshy area of seashore were studied. The concentration of salts in the root cells of each type of plant was measured. The results are shown in the diagram below.

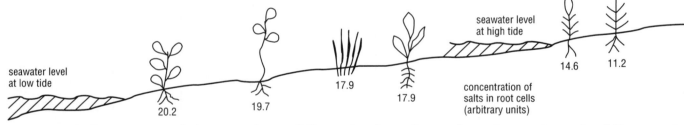

       (i)   Different types of plants survive at different levels on the seashore. Suggest how the differences in concentration of salts in their root cells adapt them for survival.   [3]
       (ii) Several of the plants had few, small leaves and deep-set stomata. Explain how these features would also help them to survive in this environment.   [4]
   (c) (i)   Explain how mineral ions enter a root hair cell from normal garden soil.   [3]
       (ii) Explain why the uptake of mineral ions in a waterlogged soil may be inhibited.   [2]

                                                                              (NEAB, Higher, June 1997)

6. The diagram shows part of a carpel in a wallflower after pollination.

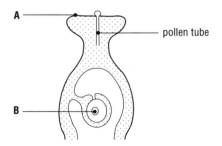

   (a) Name the parts labelled **A** and **B**.   [2]
   (b) Complete the diagram to show the path of the pollen tube up to the point where it enters structure B.   [1]
   (c) Name the process which occurs when the male and female nuclei fuse.   [1]

                                                                                (CCEA, Tier Q, June 1995)

Section
FIVE

Variation, inheritance and evolution

5.1 Variation

Most young plants and animals have similar characteristics to those of their parents. There is variation between individuals, however. Variation of characteristics is the result of:

- Genetic causes – this is because of information passed on to individuals via the male and female sex cells (gametes) from their parents, both sex cells being involved in fertilisation (see section 1.3).
- Environmental causes – this is the effect of the environment on a characteristic.
- A combination of both genetic and environmental causes.

The effect of these two can be clearly seen if we consider height in humans. The types of genes we have inherited will determine our final potential height. Whether we reach that potential height will depend on the way we develop in our environment. For example, growth will be stunted if there is severe malnutrition in early childhood.

Discontinuous variation

Here there are distinct types with no intermediate forms between them. Examples include:

- Type of blood group.
- Male or female.
- Presence or absence of ear lobes.

Continuous variation

Here there are extremes of the characteristic between which there are a range of intermediate types. Examples include height in humans, skin colour and hair texture.

Data about these types of variation can be displayed in frequency histograms (Figure 5.1.1). Most individuals are quite close to the centre of the range (the norm). The number of individuals who differ from the norm becomes smaller as the difference from the norm becomes greater.

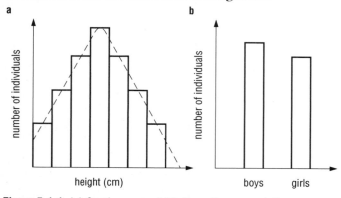

Figure 5.1.1 (**a**) Continuous and (**b**) discontinuous variation

Chromosomes and DNA

Most cells have a nucleus. In the nucleus of normal human body cells not involved in reproduction (**somatic cells**) there are 46 chromosomes (different species having different numbers). These occur in pairs (the diploid state), one of each pair having come from the father (via the sperm) and one from the mother (via the egg). This gives a total of 23 pairs of chromosomes (two sets of chromosomes). Having only one set of chromosomes, as in human gametes, is often referred to as the haploid state.

Sometimes errors occur in gamete formation resulting in one gamete having an extra chromosome (24 in all). If this gamete is involved in fertilisation the resulting individual will have 47 chromosomes and may suffer from DOWN'S SYNDROME. A person with this condition has specific features like a broad flat face, mongoloid eyes, a single palm crease and a low IQ.

The chromosomes carry the genes which control all the characteristics of the organism. Since the chromosomes occur in pairs, each nucleus usually has at least two genes controlling each characteristic.

The chromosomes are made of a chemical called DNA. The structure of DNA was discovered by Watson and Crick. DNA is a polymer, which means it is a large molecule made up of many small units. In DNA these are called NUCLEOTIDES and there are four types depending on which base they contain. These bases are identified by their letters A, C, T and G (adenine, cytosine, thymine and guanine).

The two strands of a DNA molecule are held together by chemical bonds between the bases of the nucleotides. Bonds can only be formed between C and G and between A and T. Therefore the sequence (order) of bases on one strand determines the sequence of bases on the other strand (Figure 5.1.2).

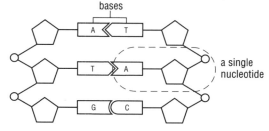

Figure 5.1.2 Base pairing in DNA

When cells divide for growth and replacement, the chromosomes (and therefore the DNA) must replicate. This begins with the two strands in the molecule unwinding as the bonds between the bases break. Free nucleotides then arrange themselves alongside the exposed bases and pair up with them – A to T and C to G, thus forming two new strands with exactly the same sequence of bases.

86

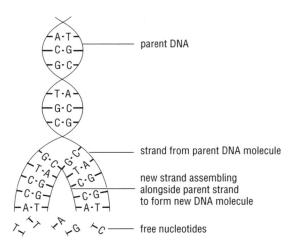

Figure 5.1.3 DNA replication

The sequence (order) of nucleotides on a strand of DNA provides the coded instructions via which the chromosomes control the assembly of amino acids in the right order to make a specific protein. It is these proteins that are involved in the development of characteristics of the organism. A gene then is a section of DNA (sequence of nucleotides) on a chromosome which controls one characteristic.

The importance of reproduction in creating variation

Asexual reproduction

This involves no sex cells or fusion of male and female gametes. Only one parent is involved, and this individual produces offspring by mitosis (see section 1.3) so that all the daughter cells are the same. This means there is no genetic variation (that is, they are genetically identical) as they have the same genes/DNA as the original parent cells. These genetically identical cells are known as **clones**. One advantage of this method of reproduction is that large numbers can be produced and quickly.

Sexual reproduction

This involves the fusion of nuclei, during fertilisation, of gametes produced by meiosis (see section 1.3) in the sex organs. This means that there will be genetic variation. Offspring will be genetically different to each other and their parents.

Mutations

A mutation is an alteration in the genetic material of a cell. Changes in the genes on chromosomes will produce new genes (alleles). These genes will produce a new/different protein.

Mutations occur naturally and randomly. During a lifetime many mutations will occur in the cells of the body as they divide repeatedly to make new cells.

Most mutations are harmful. If mutations occur in the body cells of, for example, the lungs, these altered cells may start to multiply in an uncontrolled way. This will develop into a cancer or tumour. These altered cells may remain in one place (benign tumours) or invade other parts of the body (malignant tumours). It is important to detect these abnormal cells early before they become widespread. As a result people are SCREENED (checked) to detect the early stages of breast and cervical cancer.

Surgery, radiotherapy (radiation) and chemotherapy (toxic materials) can be used to destroy or remove the abnormal cells.

Mutations in reproductive cells will be passed on to the children. The fetus may develop abnormally, for example with limbs deformed or missing. The children may die at an early stage or may be more likely to develop cancers like leukaemia.

Several factors can increase the frequency of mutations occurring, that is, they increase the number of mutations in cells. They are exposure to:

- Ultraviolet radiation.
- X-rays.
- Radiation from radioactive substances.
- A range of chemicals including mustard gas, tar from cigarettes and benzene in petrol.

Some mutations are neither beneficial nor harmful, and these are called neutral. Rarely mutations occur which in some way are beneficial to the organism, and may increase its chances of survival (see section 5.3). Such beneficial mutations will tend to spread through a population.

Quick Questions

1. What are the two types of variation? How are they different?
2. What do the terms **a)** diploid and **b)** haploid mean?
3. How many pairs of chromosomes are there in normal human somatic cells?
4. What happens to the number of chromosomes during gamete formation (meiosis)?
5. What is the name of the small units that DNA is made of?
6. How does DNA duplicate itself?
7. How does DNA control protein production?
8. Why do organisms produced by sexual reproduction show variation?
9. What is a mutation?
10. Give two examples of things that increase the frequency of mutations in cells.

5.2 Inheritance

Here are some definitions you must know:

- **Phenotype**: an organism's outward appearance; how the genes are expressed in the organism.
- **Genotype**: the genes that the cells of the organism contain.
- **Allele**: a distinct form of a gene for a certain characteristic.
- **Homozygous**: having two identical alleles for a particular characteristic.
- **Heterozygous**: having two different alleles for a particular characteristic.
- **Dominant** allele: an allele that has an effect in either the homozygous or heterozygous condition.
- **Recessive** allele: an allele that only has an effect in the homozygous condition.

Remember that most characteristics are controlled by pairs of genes and that there are different forms of genes called alleles. It is these alleles that are passed on through the gametes to the next generation.

Mendel's work

Mendel, who has been described as the father of modern genetics, lived in the middle of the last century. He knew nothing of the structure of nuclei, chromosomes or genes. But through his experiments on pea plants he was able to establish the presence of genes, which he called 'factors'.

In his simplest experiments he worked on pea plants that were homozygous or pure-bred. This means that they came from a long line of ancestors which showed the same characteristics.

Mendel first crossed pure-breeding tall plants with pure-breeding dwarf plants, collected the seeds, germinated them, allowed them to develop and noted their characteristics. He found that this first generation (the F_1 or first filial generation) were all tall plants and not intermediate between the two parental types.

He then allowed these F_1 plants to self-pollinate to produce an F_2 generation (second filial generation). In this generation he found that there were both tall and dwarf plants. The dwarf characteristic had reappeared and therefore it must have been hidden or masked in the first generation. Today we would say that the recessive allele for dwarfness had been masked by the dominant allele for tallness.

These experimental crosses can be represented by genetic diagrams as shown opposite (remember each characteristic is controlled by at least two genes, one from the male gamete and one from the female gamete).

Let T represent the allele for tallness.
Let t represent the allele for dwarfness.

Phenotypes of parents	tall	×	dwarf
Genotypes of parents	TT		tt
Gametes (produced by meiosis)	all T		all t

Genotype of offspring (F_1) (produced on fertilisation)	Tt
Phenotype of offspring	tall

Phenotypes of parents	tall	×	tall
Genotypes of parents	Tt		Tt
Gametes (produced by meiosis)	T or t		T or t

Genotypes of offspring (F_2)
(produced on fertilisation)

		male gametes	
		T	t
female gametes	T	TT	Tt
	t	Tt	tt

Phenotypes of offspring   A ratio of three tall TT, Tt and Tt to one dwarf tt

How can we establish the genotype of a tall plant?

In the above genetic cross the F_2 produced two types of genotypes for tall pea plants – TT and Tt. To identify each one we must carry out the BACKCROSS TEST. Here each tall plant is crossed with a recessive dwarf (as the genotype of this is always tt).

A With TT:

Genotypes of parents	TT	×	tt
Genotypes of gametes	T		t
Offspring		Tt	

In this cross therefore only tall offspring are produced.

B With Tt:

Genotypes of parents	Tt	×	tt
Genotypes of gametes	T or t		all t

Offspring

	T	t
t	Tt	tt

In this cross there will be a ratio of one tall to one dwarf plant. Therefore in any cross between a tall and dwarf plant that produces this ratio we can assume the tall parent must have been a HYBRID (heterozygous).

Inherited diseases

Some diseases are INHERITED. These diseases are caused by genes which have been passed on from parents to their young. There are believed to be 2300 genetic diseases. These diseases are due to some alteration of either the genes or the chromosomes. Such defective/altered genes (alleles) may be either dominant or recessive.

Examples of inherited diseases

Cystic fibrosis
This disorder affects mucus-secreting glands, especially those of the intestine or lungs. The mucus becomes thick and sticky, so that ducts become blocked. Many sufferers die at a young age.

The disease affects 1 in every 1600 babies and is caused by a recessive gene. The person must therefore be homozygous in order to have the disease. The allele that causes the disease must be passed on by both parents. Neither will have any symptoms of the disease (that is, they are carriers). Transmission from carriers to offspring is shown below:

Let *C* represent the normal allele.

Let *c* represent the cystic fibrosis allele.

Parental phenotypes	normal		normal
Parental genotypes (carriers)	*Cc*	×	*Cc*
Types of gametes produced	Ⓒ or ⓒ		Ⓒ or ⓒ

Genotypes of offspring

	C	*c*
C	*CC*	*Cc*
c	*Cc*	*cc*

cc = person with cystic fibrosis.

There is a one in four (25%) chance of the offspring having cystic fibrosis.

Huntingdon's disease
This disease (formerly known as Huntingdon's chorea) does not show symptoms until the age of 40 to 50. It then begins to affect the nervous system, causing shaking, twitching and mental deterioration. There is no known cure. The disease affects 1 in 100 000 of the population and is caused by a dominant gene and can therefore be inherited from one parent with the disorder. Both homozygous and heterozygous people for this allele will be sufferers.

Let *H* = allele for Huntingdon's disease.

Let *h* = normal allele.

People with genotypes *HH* and *Hh* will be sufferers.

Phenotypes of parents	Huntingdon's sufferer		normal
Genotypes of parents	*Hh*	×	*hh*
Gametes	Ⓗ or ⓗ		all ⓗ

Genotypes of offspring

	H	*h*
h	*Hh*	*hh*

There is a one in two (50%) chance of the offspring suffering from Huntingdon's disease.

Sickle cell anaemia
This condition is caused by an allele that shows partial recessiveness. The allele results in abnormally shaped red blood cells which cannot carry oxygen. People who are heterozygous have 60–70% of their red cells normal. Those in the homozygous state die very young or are born dead as all cells are abnormal. The heterozygous state can, however, be advantageous in regions of the world where malaria is a problem because malarial parasites cannot feed on the abnormal red blood cells and soon die. Because of this, people who have the sickle cell allele have an advantage as they are less likely to get malaria.

Determination of sex

Of the 46 chromosomes in each human nucleus, there are 44 **autosomes** and two **sex chromosomes**. The latter, as their name suggests, are involved in deciding the sex of the offspring. These sex chromosomes are known simply as X and Y chromosomes, the Y chromosome being shorter than the X chromosome.

- Females have two X chromosomes.
- Males have one X and one Y chromosome.

	Mother	Father
	XX	XY
Gametes	all Ⓧ	Ⓧ or Ⓨ

Offspring

	X	Y
X	XX	XY

There is a 50/50 chance of producing a boy or a girl.

Sex-linked inheritance

This involves genes carried on the X chromosome. If it is a defective gene, most sufferers will be male since the shorter Y chromosome carries no genes to mask the presence of any gene on the X chromosome and the chances of females being homozygous is small. Examples of such diseases include HAEMOPHILIA and COLOUR BLINDNESS.

Sufferers of haemophilia experience excessive bleeding internally. Bleeding into joints causes severe pain, and anaemia results from the slow but constant loss of blood. The disease affects 1 in 10 000 live male births.

Let H = normal allele.

Let b = allele for haemophilia.

Phenotypes of parents	normal female (carrier)		normal male	
Genotypes of parents	$X^H X^b$	$\times$	$X^H Y$	
Gametes produced	X^H or X^b		X^H or Y	

Offspring/progeny	X^H	Y
X^H	$X^H X^H$	$X^H Y$
X^b	$X^H X^b$	$X^b Y$

where

$X^b Y$ = haemophiliac male

$X^H Y$ = normal male

$X^H X^b$ = carrier female

$X^H X^H$ = normal female

Therefore there is a one in two (50%) chance that any boys will be haemophiliac.

Controlling inheritance

Selective breeding

This is sometimes called ARTIFICIAL SELECTION. Selective breeding is used to produce new varieties of organism that have the characteristics we want. For example, we can produce:

- Crop plants resistant to disease.
- Cows that produce larger milk yields.
- Tomato plants that produce small 'cherry' tomatoes.

Only those individuals showing the 'best' characteristics are allowed to breed. Transfer of gametes is often carried out artificially; for example, in farm animals by **artificial insemination**, and in plants by transfer of pollen using a special brush. This selective breeding programme may be repeated over several generations.

Selective breeding greatly reduces the number of alleles in a population, however. This in turn reduces the variation within the population. As there are fewer alleles to select from, selective breeding may mean that the species cannot survive changed conditions.

Cloning (artificial propagation)

Cloning plants

When selective breeding has produced individual plants with the desired characteristics, horticulturalists will then clone them to produce large numbers of identical plants quickly and cheaply. Cloning further reduces the number of alleles available for selective breeding as other variations of plants are not available.

- Taking CUTTINGS (see section 4.4).
- TISSUE CULTURE: small groups of cells are taken from a plant where cells are dividing rapidly, such as

root and shoot apexes. The cells are then grown on special growth medium in sterile containers. Plant hormones (growth regulators) are used to control the development of the complete plant.

Cloning animals

This has only recently become possible.

- Newly divided cells, which are not yet specialised, are removed from the animal. These are capable of reproducing to produce the whole organism. These are the donor cells.
- The donor cells are allowed to multiply.
- The nuclei are removed from 'foster' eggs.
- The donor cell nuclei (all identical) are transferred to the 'foster' eggs.
- The foster eggs with donor nuclei are implanted into the uteri of surrogate females.

Another method involves removing embryos at a very early stage of development, separating the cells and then transplanting the identical embryos into the uteri of host mothers. This method has been used successfully for cattle.

Genetic engineering

This is the most advanced technique involved in modern day breeding programmes. Here, by using specific enzymes called RESTRICTION ENDONUCLEASES, we can cut out specific genes from chromosomes and transfer them to bacterial cells using plasmids (small circular pieces of DNA that can exist inside a bacterium). The transferred gene or section of DNA will continue to function in the bacterium and cause it to produce the specific protein that the gene codes for. The bacterium has no use for the new protein it makes and therefore it secretes it to the outside. By culturing the bacteria on a large scale, commercial quantities of the required protein can be obtained. This process of GENETIC ENGINEERING can be used to obtain large and cheap supplies of drugs and hormones, including FACTOR VIII for haemophiliacs and INSULIN for diabetics (Figure 5.2.1).

We can use bacteria and viruses as carriers of genes. For example, we can insert a gene for resistance to a certain plant disease into a bacterium (*Agrobacterium*). The bacteria is then allowed to infect crop plants, such as peas, which will then be resistant. We can use genetically engineered viruses to kill pest species.

Genes can also be transferred to the cells of animals or plants at an early stage in their development so that they can develop with desired characteristics, such as resistance to fungal diseases in certain types of potato plant. This reduces the need for the use of pesticides and therefore reduces pollution.

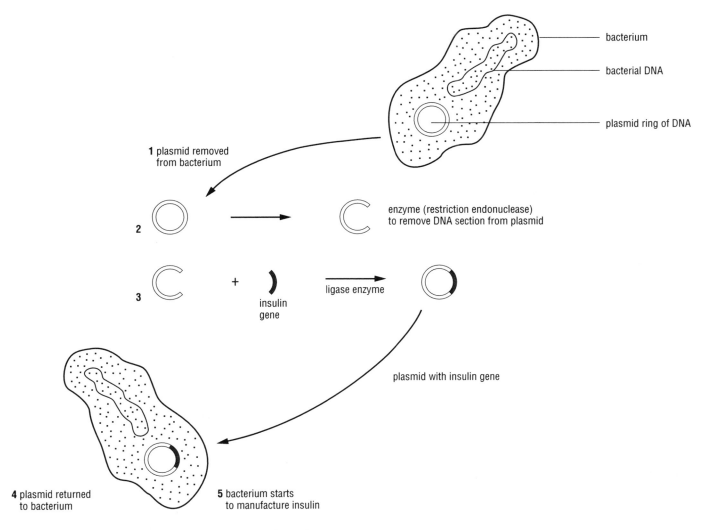

Figure 5.2.1 Genetic engineering: insulin production by bacteria

Transgenic animals

Transgenic sheep and cattle have been produced, in which human genes have been transferred into the milk-producing cells. These cells then secrete the human protein coded for by the gene into their milk. This milk can then be collected and the human protein separated from it.

Ethical issues

There are undoubted benefits arising from genetic engineering, but there are possible dangers and also ethical problems. These include:

- The possibility that altered genes may be transferred to other organisms in natural ecosystems, where they may have harmful effects.
- The possibility that mutation of the altered genes will occur so that effectiveness is lost or there are harmful effects.
- Should we continue research that would allow us to introduce into human zygotes genes for desirable characteristics, and remove disease-causing genes?

Quick Questions

1. What do the words 'genotype' and 'phenotype' mean?
2. **a)** What is a gene?
   b) What is an allele?
3. What is the difference between dominant and recessive alleles?
4. What is meant by the term 'heterozygous'?
5. What sex chromosomes are present in:
   a) A human female?
   b) A human male?
6. What is meant by the term 'sex-linked disease'? Give two examples.
7. What are the symptoms of Huntingdon's disease?
8. What is selective breeding?
9. Give two ways in which plants can be cloned.
10. How can genetic engineering help us to produce large quantities of insulin cheaply?

5.3 Evolution

This term refers to the changes that take place in organisms over a long period of time.

The theory of evolution suggests that organisms change or evolve over time, and that existing organisms have evolved from simpler ancestors which have, over generations, become different and more complex. These ancestral simpler organisms are thought to have developed more than three billion years ago. Many of the ancestral species have become extinct and can only be studied by looking at their fossil remains. Extinction of these species may be the result of:

- Severe changes in **abiotic factors** of the organism's environment, such as temperature and humidity, which reduced their chances of survival.
- Changes in the **biotic factors** of an organism's environment, such as new predators, new diseases or new competitors.

The fossil record

Evidence for evolution can be found in the fossil record. These are the 'remains' of animals and plants which can be found in rocks and may have been formed in one of the following ways:

- From the hard parts of animals which do not decay easily.
- From parts of animals or plants which have not decayed because one or more of the conditions needed for decay are absent.
- The replacement of parts of the plant or animal by other materials, such as minerals, as they decay.

Fossils are found in layers of rock. The layers can now be dated and it can be shown that the oldest layers of rock contain the oldest fossils. It is possible to follow the evolution of, for example, land mammals from ancestors that lived in the sea.

Theory of natural selection

The theory of evolution is based on work carried out by Charles Darwin, who stated that there was a 'struggle for survival' between the members of a population. There will be competition for resources, predation and disease and large numbers of the population will die. His work led on to the theory of natural selection which helps to explain how evolution works:

- In any natural population there will be variation between individuals. This variation is the result of MUTATIONS producing different types of allele for each gene.

- Those individuals with variations of a character that are BEST ADAPTED to the environment are more likely to survive and reproduce, thus passing on their alleles to their offspring. NATURAL SELECTION will select those individuals who are best adapted.
- If the environment changes, then the new conditions will favour certain variations more than others. NATURAL SELECTION will again now SELECT out those few individuals best adapted to the new conditions. These will survive to breed and therefore pass on their favourable alleles.
- Eventually the characteristics of the population will change. This will, over many generations, lead to evolution of a new species. (A **species** is a population of similar organisms which can breed successfully and produce fertile offspring).

Examples of natural selection in action

One of the earliest horse-like animals differed from the modern horse in three ways:

1 It was much smaller.
2 It had well-developed digits (fingers/toes).
3 Its teeth were not developed for grinding its food.

These three characteristics changed as the environment changed over a period of fifty million years. This was because:

- The marshy wooded country was gradually replaced by a drier type. Those horses that were taller than the rest survived, as they could get a better view of the surrounding land and see predators more quickly.
- The increased size of the animals and drier habitat did not favour those animals with wider splayed-out feet. Animals with narrower feet survived better because they could run faster and therefore escape from predators more easily.
- The change in vegetation from soft plant material to coarser grasses favoured those horses that had teeth which could grind the food. Therefore, those horses with a wider grinding area and deepening of the teeth survived better as they could make better use of the food.

Thus, as the environment changed those animals that had these favourable variations were able to survive to breed and pass on these advantageous alleles (Figure 5.3.1).

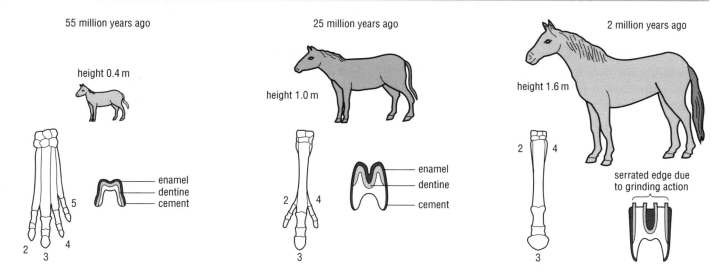

Figure 5.3.1 The evolution of the modern horse: changes in body size, limb bones and teeth

The Galapagos Islands in the Pacific have populations of different species of finch. These are all thought to have originated from a single species which had migrated from South America. Each island has a different type of food available. Natural selection on the different islands favoured/selected those finches with beaks best adapted for catching or eating the food source on each island.

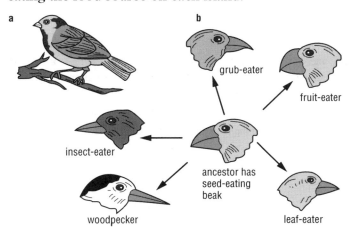

Figure 5.3.2 (a) One of the Galapagos finches. (b) The first species on the Galapagos islands is thought to have had a beak adapted to eating seeds. Individuals of this species then flew to other islands where those with a slightly different beak, who could eat new foods, had a competitive edge. Up to 16 species now exist

The peppered moth (*Biston betularia*) exists in two forms, a light speckled form and a much darker form. Both rely on camouflage to protect them from predatory birds. Before 1850 the dark form was rare since dark individuals would be easily seen by birds while resting on tree-trunks. The possession of the alleles for darkness was disadvantageous and therefore selected against. With the rapid development of industry after 1850, the number of

darker forms increased in industrial areas. Nineteenth-century industry produced a great deal of soot and smoke which collected on tree trunks; this was an environmental change. The speckled forms were now visible and eaten more frequently by predators. The possession of the allele for darkness was now advantageous as it gave the dark forms camouflage. More dark forms survived so in those areas most individuals now carry the allele for dark colour.

Figure 5.3.3 The light and dark forms of the peppered moth (*Biston betularia*)

Bacteria have become resistant to antibiotics by the same process (see section 2.10). Widespread overuse of antibiotics has selected against any bacteria susceptible to, for example, penicillin. Only those that have alleles giving resistance survive to reproduce. Over many generations, therefore, the number of resistant types has greatly increased.

Quick Questions

1 What does the theory of evolution suggest?
2 Give reasons why species become extinct.
3 What are fossils?
4 Which organisms in a population will be selected for by natural selection?
5 Why have resistant strains of bacteria evolved?
6 What is meant by the term 'species'?

5.4 Classification of living organisms

Living organisms are put into groups, classified depending on important features that they have. Those with similar features are put in the same group. Sometimes it is difficult to decide how to classify some organisms and as a result groupings do change and new names for groups are used. The most recent system used is based on five Kingdoms, listed below.

Monera: this Kingdom includes all bacteria (Figure 5.4.1) and the blue-green algae. Their genetic material is not organised into a nucleus.

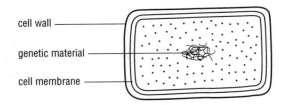

Figure 5.4.1 A typical bacterium

Protoctista: the cells of these organisms have nuclei. This Kingdom includes single-celled organisms such as *Euglena* and *Amoeba*, and also the algae, which are photosynthetic organisms with a cell structure similar to that of plants but they lack roots, stems, leaves and vascular tissue (xylem and phloem). Algae show great diversity and examples include *Spirogyra* and seaweeds like *Fucus* (Figure 5.4.2).

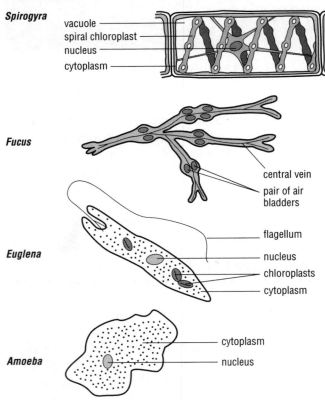

Figure 5.4.2 Protoctista

Fungi: these have no chlorophyll and therefore live on organic material already synthesised by other living organisms. Most have a saprophytic mode of nutrition. The group includes yeasts and moulds (such as those that grow on stale bread), mushrooms and toadstools (Figure 5.4.3). Reproduction in fungi involves the production of spores.

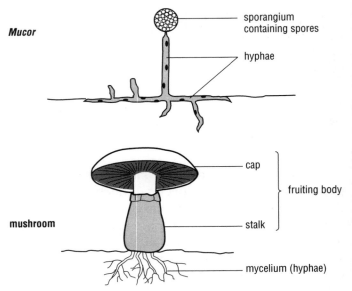

Figure 5.4.3 Fungi

Plants: this kingdom includes:

* BRYOPHYTES, such as mosses (Figure 5.4.4), consist of stem and leaves without specialised vascular tissue. Rhizoids are present and spores are produced. The main plant carries out sexual reproduction.

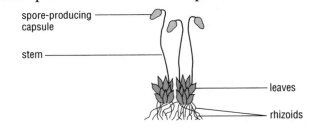

Figure 5.4.4 *Funaria*, a moss (bryophyte)

* PTERIDOPHYTES, such as ferns (Figure 5.4.5), consist of roots, stems and leaves with specialised vascular tissue and spores are produced. The main plant uses asexual reproduction.

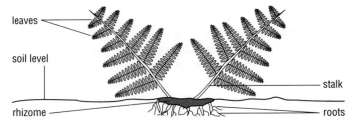

Figure 5.4.5 A fern (pteridophyte)

- SPERMATOPHYTES (angiosperms) have roots, stems and leaves with specialised vascular tissue, flowers and seeds are produced. The group includes all flowering plants, from dandelions to oak trees (Figure 5.4.6).

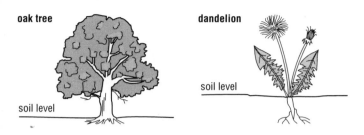

Figure 5.4.6 Two angiosperms

Animals: this Kingdom is divided into many diverse groups.

The INVERTEBRATES are those animals that do not have a backbone and whose nerve cord is ventral. Some examples are:

- ANNELIDS, such as earthworms, have segmentation and chaetae (bristles used in locomotion).
- ARTHROPODS have an exoskeleton and jointed legs and show cephalisation (well-developed sensory structures and feeding organs at the front end of the body). Examples include crabs, spiders and insects like beetles, butterflies and bees. The group with the largest number of species, the INSECTS, have three parts to their body, together with three pairs of legs and two pairs of wings.
- MOLLUSCS, which usually have an exoskeleton in a shell form. Garden snails and mussels are examples.

CHORDATES have a dorsal nerve cord usually protected by a backbone. Some of the main groups are:

- BONY FISH, which have gills, fins, scales and large numbers of eggs produced with external fertilisation. Examples include cod and goldfish.
- AMPHIBIANS, which have lungs in the adult form, moist skin, external fertilisation in water and production of many eggs. Examples include frogs and toads.
- REPTILES, which have scales, internal fertilisation and a relatively small number of shelled eggs laid on dry land. Examples include snakes, crocodiles, lizards and tortoises.
- MAMMALS, which have mammary glands, that produce milk, hair, ear pinna, internal fertilisation and development, parental care and a constant body temperature. Examples include humans, whales, rats and bats.
- BIRDS, which have feathers, wings, a beak and, like mammals, can regulate their body temperature. They reproduce by laying eggs. Examples include sparrows, blackbirds, penguins and ostriches.

Use of keys

Keys are used to identify living organisms. They are usually made up of paired numbered sentences which describe features of organisms. To use a key:

- Look carefully at the specimen, photograph or drawing.
- Read the first pair of descriptive sentences and choose the one that fits your specimen.
- This sentence will have a number which tells you which pair of descriptive sentences to read next.
- Repeat this process until the name of the organism is given.

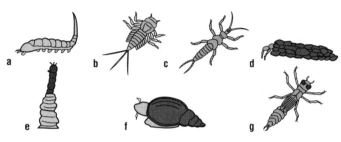

1	tail has long extensions	go to 2
	no extensions on the tail	go to 4
2	tail has one extension	**rat-tailed maggot**
	tail has more than one extension	go to 3
3	tail has two extensions	**stonefly nymph**
	tail has three extensions	**mayfly nymph**
4	animal is inside a case or shell	go to 5
	animal is not inside a case or shell . . .	go to 6
5	case made of many small pieces	**caddis fly larva**
	shell is made of one piece	**water snail**
6	animal has three pairs of legs	**dragonfly nymph**
	animal has no legs	**bloodworm**

To use this key, look at one animal, then ask each question and answer in turn. For example, look at animal **a**:

1 does the tail have long extensions on it? . . . . . . yes, so go to **2**
2 does the tail have only one extension? . . . . yes, so it is a rat-tailed maggot and so on.

Now look at animal **b**:

1 does the tail have long extensions on it? . . . . . . yes, so go to **2**
2 does the tail have only one extension? . . . . no, it is not a rat-tailed maggot
   does the tail have more than one extension? . . . yes, so go to **3**
3 does the tail have two extensions? . . . . no, it is not a stonefly nymph
   does the tail have three extensions? . . . . yes, it is a mayfly nymph and so on.

Figure 5.4.7 A key for some freshwater animals

Quick Questions

1 Use the key to identify animals **c** to **g** in the diagram.
2 Which group of plants has stems and leaves but lacks vascular tissue, has rhizoids and produces spores?
3 Give an example of an organism belonging to the algae (Kingdom Protoctista).
4 Give two features found in all arthropods.
5 Which chordate group includes animals which have lungs in the adult, moist skin, reproduce in water and produce many eggs?

Section Five: Examination Questions

1. The diagram shows part of a DNA molecule.

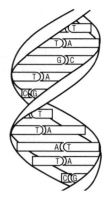

(a) Describe the structure of the DNA molecule. [2]

(b) Name the two scientists who discovered the structure of DNA. [2]

(c) Complete the diagram to show how DNA replicates. [3]

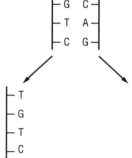

(CCEA, Tier R, June 1996)

2. The following diagram shows red bone marrow tissue producing mutant cells which multiply and become cancer cells.

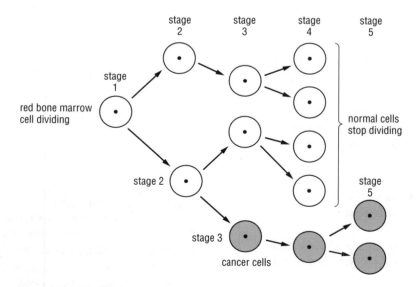

(a) (i) Between which **two** stages has mutation taken place? [1]

    (ii) What is meant by **mutation**? [1]

(b) (i) Suggest **two** causes of this type of mutation. [2]

    (ii) Explain how natural selection may cause a mutation to become common several generations later. [4]

(WJEC, Higher, Specimen)

3. A plant breeder crossed Californian poppies. One had yellow flowers and the other had white flowers. This was how the cross was carried out.

  The flower buds of a yellow-flowering plant were cut open and the immature stamens were removed. Pollen from the white-flowering plant was transferred, using a paint brush, to the stigmas of the yellow flowers. A paper bag was tied over these yellow flowers until the seed pods had developed. The seeds were collected and sown in labelled pots. The resulting hybrids were all white-flowering.

  Answer the following questions using the information above and your own knowledge.

(a) Why were the stamens removed from the yellow-flowering plant? [1]

(b) Why were paper bags tied over the yellow flowers? [1]

(c) Suggest a reason why **all** the hybrids had white flowers. [1]

A further 2000 crosses like the one described were made. All the resulting plants were white-flowering with one exception, which was a yellow-flowering plant.

(d) Suggest **two** explanations for this one exception. [2]

The hybrid white poppies were then crossed with the original yellow poppies.

(e) (i) [Use the space below] to show the results of this cross. Use the symbols **f** and **F** to represent the genes for flower colour. [4]

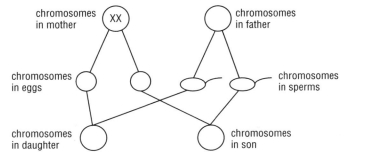

Parent plant appearance: white hybrid   ×   yellow

Genotypes: ×

Offspring:

  (ii) If 60 offspring were produced, what is the likely number that would have yellow flowers? [1]

(MEG (Suffolk), Special, June 1995)

4. **(a)** Complete the diagram to show how the sex of a child depends on the chromosomes the child inherits.

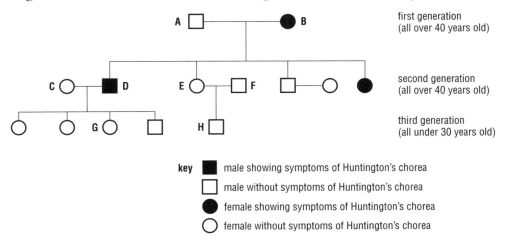

[3]

(b) The diagram shows the inheritance of Huntingdon's chorea in a family.

key ■ male showing symptoms of Huntington's chorea
     □ male without symptoms of Huntington's chorea
     ● female showing symptoms of Huntington's chorea
     ○ female without symptoms of Huntington's chorea

  Symptoms of Huntingdon's chorea usually develop between the ages of 35 and 40. What is the chance that the following will develop Huntingdon's chorea?

  1 **G** ....   **2** **H** ....

  Explain the reasons for your answer as fully as you can. You may use genetic diagrams if you wish. [6]

(NEAB, Tier R, June 1995)

5. (a) Haemophilia is a disease which prevents blood clotting properly.

Normal blood clotting is controlled by a dominant allele (H). The haemophiliac condition is controlled by the recessive allele (h).

The diagram in box 1 shows the sex chromosomes of a haemophiliac male and the position of allele (h). In box 2 draw the sex chromosomes and label the blood-clotting allele or alleles of a female carrier.

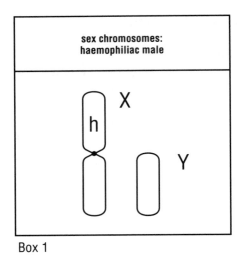

Box 1

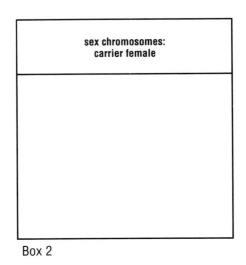

Box 2

[2]

(b) The family tree below shows some people with normal blood clotting, some who are haemophiliacs and others who are 'unknown' for this factor.

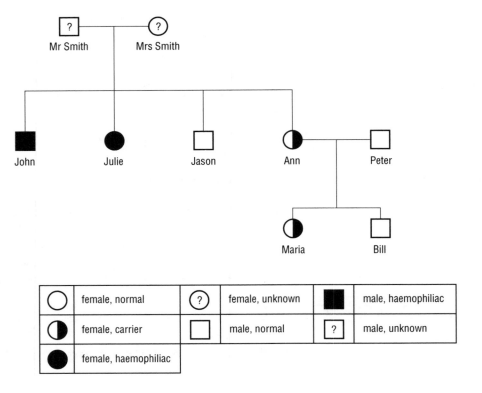

◯	female, normal	?	female, unknown	■	male, haemophiliac
◖	female, carrier	□	male, normal	?	male, unknown
●	female, haemophiliac				

Use the information in the diagram to answer the following questions.

(i) What are the genotypes for Mr and Mrs Smith? Explain how you arrived at your answer. [3]

(ii) What is the probability of Ann and Peter producing a haemophiliac female? Explain how you arrived at your answer. [3]

(London, Higher, Specimen)

6. The pedigree shows the inheritance of red–green colour blindness in humans.
X^N represents the chromosome for normal vision.
X^n represents the chromosome for red–green colour blindness.

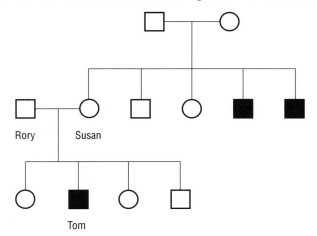

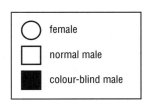

○ female

□ normal male

■ colour-blind male

(a) What term is used to describe this type of inheritance? [1]
(b) What do the N and n represent in the genetic symbols? [1]
(c) What are the genotypes of individuals Tom and Rory? [2]
(d) What is Susan's genotype? Explain your answer. [4]
(e) In humans the disorders haemophilia and red–green colour blindness are both inherited in the same way, yet there are more colour-blind people than haemophiliacs. Explain this difference. [2]

(CCEA, Tier R, June 1996)

7. The drawings below show three dogs. They are all members of the **same species**.

A

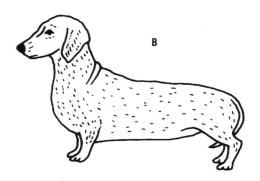

B

C

(a) What does it mean to be in the *same* species? [2]
(b) Breeders of dog **B** have to produce dogs for showing that are under 5 kg. Describe how breeders can use **selective breeding** to increase the chances of obtaining dogs of this size. [3]

(SEG, Higher, Specimen)

8. Read the extract.

Super-bug may hit the price of coffee

The coffee bean borer, a pest of the coffee crop, can be controlled by the pesticide endosulfan. However, strains of the insect that are up to 100 times more resistant to the pesticide have emerged on the South Pacific island of New Caledonia.

For full resistance to be passed on to an offspring, two copies of the new resistance allele should be inherited, one from each parent.

There is much inbreeding, with brother–sister matings happening in every generation, so it takes only a few generations before all the descendants of a single resistant female have inherited two copies of the resistance allele. If this resistance spreads from New Caledonia, it will mean the loss of a major control method. This will present a serious threat to the international coffee industry.

(a) Suggest how the allele for resistance to endosulfan may have arisen. [1]

(b) How would you expect the proportion of normal coffee bean borers in New Caledonia to change over the next few years? Explain why this change will take place. [3]

(c) Explain why 'it takes only a few generations before all the descendants of a single resistant female have inherited two copies of the resistance allele'. [3]

(d) Most people have a gene which produces a protein called CFTR. CFTR enables the cells lining the lungs to work efficiently. In people suffering from cystic fibrosis this gene is faulty; it produces a protein which lacks just one of the 1480 amino acids found in CFTR.

    (i) Name the molecule which carries the genetic information for producing proteins such as CFTR. [1]

    (ii) Explain how this molecule is responsible for the structure of proteins such as CFTR. [3]

(e) Scientists are investigating the use of genetic engineering techniques to produce CFTR for cystic fibrosis sufferers. Describe briefly the techniques which are used in genetic engineering. [3]

(NEAB, Higher, June 1997)

9. The first birds evolved from reptiles. Like reptiles they had teeth. Modern birds have no teeth, and the bones of the skull and beak have air spaces inside them.

The drawings show a reconstruction of the skeleton of a fossil bird, and the skeleton of a modern pigeon.

fossil bird   modern pigeon

(a) Describe **two** differences between the skeletons of the fossils and modern birds that can be seen in the drawings. [2]

(b) (i) Suggest why it is an advantage to modern birds to have air spaces inside the bones and beak. [2]

    (ii) Explain, as fully as you can, how birds may have evolved air spaces inside the bones and beak as a result of natural selection. [5]

(NEAB, Level R, June 1996)

10. The diagrams show the two phenotypes of the peppered moth.

melanic phenotype   speckled phenotype

(a) Which type of variation is shown by the peppered moth? [1]

(b) The bar chart shows the proportions of the two phenotypes, found resting on tree-trunks during the day, in a smoke-polluted woodland.

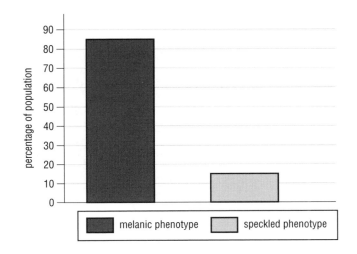

(i) Explain the proportions of the two phenotypes. [3]

(ii) Suggest what would happen to this population of moths if smoke pollution was reduced. [1]

(CCEA, Tier R, June 1996)

11. The drawings show a wild pig and an English Large White pig. The drawings are to the same scale.

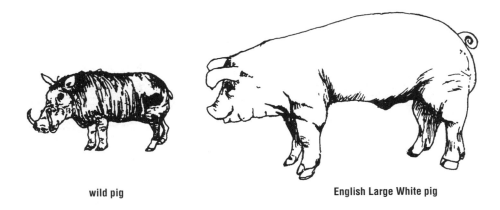

wild pig   English Large White pig

(a) The English Large White pig has been produced from the wild pig by selective breeding. Use information from the drawings to give **two** characteristics which farmers selected when breeding the English Large White pig. [2]

(b) Give **two** advantages of producing new breeds of animals. [2]

(NEAB, Level I, June 1997)

12. The drawings show five animals.

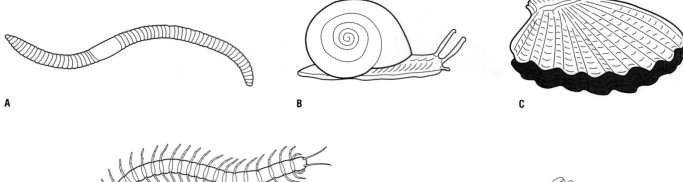

A B C

D E

Use the information in the drawings to complete the key by filling in the appropriate letter in each box.

1	segmented body	go to **2**
	body not segmented	go to **4**
2	wings present	☐
	wings absent	go to **3**
3	chaetae visible	☐
	chaetae not visible	☐
4	shell coiled	☐
	shell not coiled	☐

[5]

(CCEA, Tier Q, June 1996)

13. The drawings show a bryophyte and a pteridophyte.

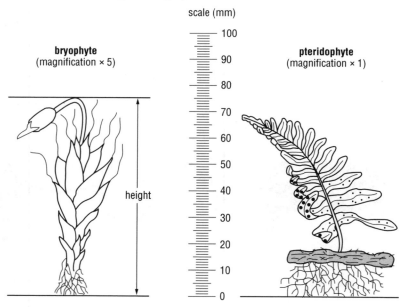

scale (mm)

bryophyte
(magnification × 5)

pteridophyte
(magnification × 1)

height

(a) Calculate the height of the bryophyte using the scale and magnification provided. Show your working. [3]

(b) Name **two** structures found in a pteridophyte but not in a bryophyte. [2]

(c) Give **one** way pteridophytes and bryophytes differ from angiosperms. [1]

(CCEA, Tier R, June 1997)

Section SIX

Living things in their environment

6.1 Adaptation and competition

Here are some important definitions:

- **Habitat**: this is a place/area where an organism lives. The habitat of a sea anemone is a rock pool, the habitat of a woodlouse is under fallen logs.
- **Environment**: every habitat has certain conditions which make it suitable for some organisms but not for others. These conditions are the organisms' environment. It includes physical (abiotic) features, such as temperature and light availability, and living (biotic) features, which would be the other plant and animal species living in the same habitat.
- **Population**: this is the name given to a group of organisms of the same species living in the same area, such as the population of woodlice living in a certain wood.
- **Community**: this term describes all the plant and animal species living together in the same habitat; for example, all the trees, grasses, birds, mammals, woodlice and other organisms living in a certain wood make up a community.
- **Ecosystem**: this term describes the community *and* its environment. We can describe, for example, freshwater pond ecosystems, saltmarsh ecosystems and so on.

Animal and plant distribution

Many factors determine whether or not an organism can survive in a particular environment. Plants and animals can only live, grow and reproduce in environments where conditions are suitable and when conditions are suitable. This explains why we see different species of animals and plants growing in different areas and at different times of the year. We find palm trees growing in the tropics and not in the Arctic. In England we find daffodils and bluebells in spring and roses in the summer. Physical (abiotic) factors that affect distribution include:

- Temperature.
- Amount of light.
- Availability of water.
- Availability of oxygen and carbon dioxide.
- Availability of breeding sites.
- Availability of nutrients in the soil.

Sampling an ecosystem

Various techniques can be used to collect animals:

- Nets: the type to be used depends on the type of organism to be collected. Large sweep nets can be used for flying insects. Kitchen sieves can be used to sample aquatic environments. Nets with a very fine mesh are needed to collect plankton.

- Pooter: this may be used if specimens are very small and delicate.
- Pit-fall traps: these are used to collect ground-dwelling organisms such as beetles. Traps can be baited to attract carnivores. They must be checked regularly or some specimens may be lost by being eaten by carnivores in the trap.

Use of quadrats

Having collected specimens from an ecosystem the next stage is to estimate how many of each species is present and perhaps their distribution. The most commonly used piece of apparatus is the quadrat. This is a square usually with sides of 0.5 m, which is used to study both animals and plants.

To estimate population size the quadrat is placed randomly on the ground and the number of a species in the area it covers is counted; alternatively the percentage cover is estimated. As much of the area must be sampled as possible.

To study distribution you would use quadrats along a transect, a line from one point to another across the area (Figure 6.1.1). A transect will give information about how the numbers and kinds of species change as the environment changes.

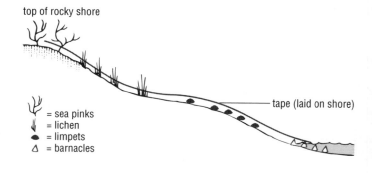

top of rocky shore

= sea pinks
= lichen
= limpets
= barnacles

tape (laid on shore)

Figure 6.1.1 A transect of a rocky shore ecosystem

Adaptations

Plants and animals have adaptations that allow them to survive in their particular environment. The more extreme the environment, the more specialised the adaptations become.

Animals living in polar environments, such as arctic foxes, polar bears and penguins, may have:

- A small surface area to volume ratio.
- Thick insulating coats.
- Thick layers of subcutaneous (under the skin) fat.

These features help to reduce heat loss. In addition the animals are camouflaged by having coats that are white either all year round (as is the polar bear) or just in the winter (as with the snowshoe hare).

In contrast animals living in desert environments, like the kangaroo rat and camel, may have:

- A large surface area to volume ratio. Having enlarged ears makes the surface area bigger.
- Little subcutaneous fat, as in the camel, it may be restricted to one part of the body to reduce insulating effects.

These features tend to increase the body's heat loss.

Plants that live in arid (dry) conditions are adapted to reducing water loss and obtaining maximum water from the soil (see section 4.3). They may:

- Have leaves with small surface areas.
- Have very large root systems.
- Store water in specialised cells.

Plants must have space to ensure they have enough water, minerals and especially light for photosynthesis. Woodland plants like the bluebell overcome the threat of light shortage by having a short life-cycle, which is completed early in the year, before the leaves of the bushes and trees emerge.

Competition and population size in communities

If several organisms of the same species or of different species share the same habitat then they will compete for resources.

- Plants will compete for space, water, light and a supply of minerals.
- Animals will compete for food, space for breeding/nesting and water.

The size of a population of an organism in a community will be affected by:

- The availability of resources like food and minerals.
- Competition for these resources.
- Predation/grazing.
- Disease.
- Balance between death rate and birth rate.
- **Emigration** and **immigration**.

In a community the sizes of populations of predators and their prey are closely linked. If the population of prey animals is high, more food is available to the predators; more predators survive and breed successfully and their population increases. As a result, more prey animals will be eaten and consequently prey numbers will fall. Therefore there will be less food available for the predators, the competition will be greater and as a result more predators will die.

It is possible to identify phases in the growth of newly established populations in a new environment. Figure 6.1.2 shows what happened after the introduction of rabbits to a remote island:

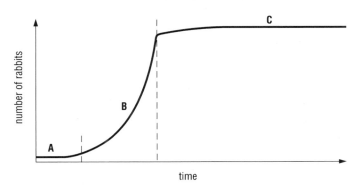

Figure 6.1.2 Variations in an island population of rabbits

- Phase **A**: the rabbit population is low and is still becoming established/adapted to the new environment.
- Phase **B**: resources are plentiful, so there is little competition between the rabbits. There are few predators. At this stage other herbivore populations may be declining if the rabbits are successfully competing against them for food.
- Phase **C**: the rabbit population is so large that there is greater competition for food, water and space. Predator numbers have now also increased. Further population growth will now be limited.

The introduction of a new species into an environment can have dramatic effects on existing populations. For example, the introduction of a new species of carp into the Murray river in Australia has greatly reduced the populations of other fish. The carp is a very successful competitor for food and has no predators, so its population growth has been rapid.

Rhododendrons were introduced into Britain about 200 years ago as ornamental shrubs. They cast such a dense shade that no other plants can grow underneath them.

Quick Questions

1. What is a habitat?
2. What do we call a group of organisms of the same species living in the same place?
3. What is a community?
4. What is an ecosystem?
5. List four physical factors that affect the distribution of plants and animals.
6. What sort of adaptive features are seen in animals that live in polar regions?
7. What is the advantage of plants such as bluebells having a short life-cycle?
8. What resources do plants compete for?
9. Why are sizes of predator and prey populations closely linked?
10. What could be the effect of introducing a new species of animal or plant into an area?

6.2 Human impact on the environment

Human populations

Unlike populations of other species, the human population continues to grow at the rate of about 2% per year. In the past the growth of human populations has been limited by disease, war and famine.

The growth rate of any population, including that of humans, depends on the balance between death rate and birth rate. If the death rate is higher than the birth rate the population will decline. If the birth rate is higher than the death rate the population will increase.

Clearly, any factor that reduces death rate or increases **life expectancy** in humans will cause a rapid population growth. Such factors include:

- Improved food supply and quality.
- Improved living conditions like better housing and sanitation.
- Provision of clean water supplies for drinking.
- Medical care, such as hospitals, immunisation, new technology and drugs.

The growth of the human population has had a dramatic effect on the environment. As the population grows:

- It needs more food; therefore more land must be used for agriculture and there must be a greater yield of food from the land.
- It needs more raw materials to make goods such as cars and televisions.
- It needs more fuel for use in homes and in industry. Much of this fuel is fossil fuel.
- It produces more toxic waste.
- It needs more space, for housing, shops and schools, for example.

All these demands put great pressures on the environment.

The greenhouse effect and global warming

The composition of the Earth's atmosphere is slowly changing. There is an increase in the concentration of the so-called 'greenhouse gases'. The most important are carbon dioxide and methane. Less important are oxides of nitrogen. This increase is producing GLOBAL WARMING.

The Earth receives short-wave (UV) radiant energy from the Sun. The Earth's surface radiates energy of longer wavelength (infra-red). The greenhouse gases make it more difficult for this energy to penetrate the atmosphere and it becomes trapped.

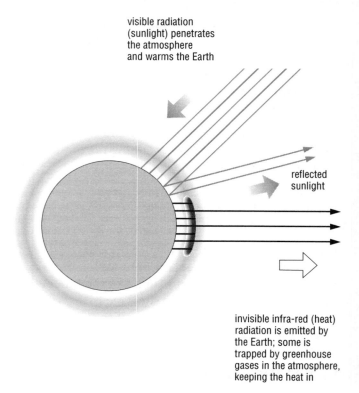

visible radiation (sunlight) penetrates the atmosphere and warms the Earth

reflected sunlight

invisible infra-red (heat) radiation is emitted by the Earth; some is trapped by greenhouse gases in the atmosphere, keeping the heat in

Figure 6.2.1 The greenhouse effect

This 'greenhouse effect' is a good thing. It allows life as we know it to exist on Earth, and without it we would all freeze. The *increase* in the effect – global warming – is the problem. The increase in the concentration of greenhouse gases is increasing the greenhouse effect and it is thought that the temperature of the Earth is slowly rising. This may cause climatic changes and the polar ice caps may melt. The result of this could be:

- Sea levels may rise.
- Rain and wind patterns may change.
- Extremes of weather may occur, leading to drought and flooding.

Causes of the increase in the greenhouse effect

- Burning of fossil fuels (coal, oil and gas) releases carbon dioxide into the atmosphere.
- As trees are cut down (deforestation) the amount of carbon dioxide removed from the atmosphere by plants for photosynthesis falls. Logs are then burned and more carbon dioxide is produced. Any remains are decomposed by bacteria, thus adding yet more carbon dioxide to the atmosphere.
- Large herds of cattle produce methane.
- Rice paddy fields also produce methane.

Deforestation

Vast areas of forest, particularly tropical rain forest, are being cut down to make way for houses, agricultural land, quarries and mines. Deforestation has several effects:

- It is one of the causes of the increase in the greenhouse effect.
- As the trees are removed the remaining thin layer of soil is eroded by rainfall.
- Soil washed from hillsides is deposited in lakes and rivers, causing them to silt up. As a result the paths of rivers can be diverted or blocked leading to flooding.
- Low-lying coastal land is flooded as rivers swell, since less water is removed as it flows through forested regions.
- Less transpiration from trees causes reduced cloud formation and therefore less rainfall. This can lead to other areas becoming more arid.
- Reduced species diversity: removing trees destroys the habitats of large numbers of species. Some of these may become extinct.
- Extinction of species means that we have lost a potential source of chemicals which could be used to treat disease.

The effects of population growth

An ever-increasing human population demands more food, a greater diversity of foods and better-quality food products. Farmers are therefore trying to increase yield and quality of their crops. As a result:

- Hedges and farm buildings are removed to create larger fields for the easier use of farm machinery. This destroys the habitats of many species, including in Britain the barn owl and other natural predators of crop pests. Soil is also more easily eroded by wind and rain.
- Farmers grow vast areas of the same crop (**monoculture**). Grass and meadowland are ploughed up and planted with wheat or barley, for example. This reduces species diversity and gives crop pests an almost limitless supply of food, allowing them to multiply and spread rapidly. This increases the need to use pesticides.
- The removal of hedges, the use of monoculture and the need to remove weeds have all led to increased use of pesticides. These can be washed into lakes and rivers, perhaps contaminating water supplies. The chemicals may accumulate in food chains, with the concentration of toxin increasing at each trophic level to a point where it can cause death or reproductive failure of animals at the end of food chains (Figure 6.2.2 – this was the case with the golden eagle in Scotland). The pesticides

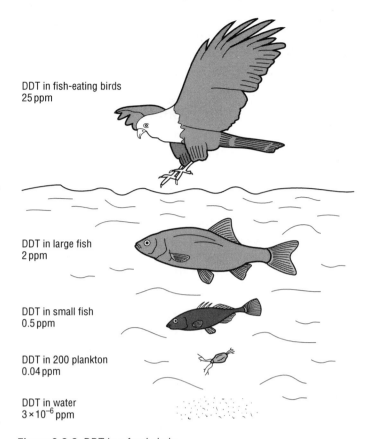

DDT in fish-eating birds
25 ppm

DDT in large fish
2 ppm

DDT in small fish
0.5 ppm

DDT in 200 plankton
0.04 ppm

DDT in water
3×10^{-6} ppm

Figure 6.2.2 DDT in a food chain

can also kill beneficial species including natural predators, increasing the need for more pesticides.
- Farmers use fertilisers to replace minerals taken from the soil by plants. Intensive farming means fields are no longer left 'fallow'.

Fertilisers contain NITRATE and PHOSPHATE. Although some is absorbed by plant roots, much runs off into streams and rivers or may percolate down to the water table. The effects of overuse of fertilisers are:

- Soil crumb structure is destroyed so that it is more easily eroded by rainfall.
- Nitrates may accumulate in drinking water. This has been linked to slow development in children. The nitrate reduces the ability of the blood to carry oxygen. There is also thought to be a possible link to stomach cancer.
- The nitrate and phosphate encourage plant growth in the rivers, particularly floating microscopic algae, causing an ALGAL BLOOM. This reduces the amount of light reaching plants in the water. The algae and plants die. Saprophytic bacteria decompose them, using oxygen. The **biochemical oxygen demand (BOD)** (the amount of oxygen needed to support respiration in the river) increases. The bacterial population will grow, rapidly deoxygenating the water, and as a result fish and other animals suffocate and die. This process is called **eutrophication**.

In addition, overfishing due to improved fishing techniques, introduced because of the rising demand for fish, has dramatically reduced fish stocks like herring and cod in the North Sea.

The effects of industry and cars

Acid rain

Much of industry depends on the use of FOSSIL FUELS for energy. As well as producing carbon dioxide (with its associated greenhouse effect), sulphur dioxide is also produced. Oxides of nitrogen are produced by power stations and vehicle exhausts. All of these gases in solution form ACID RAIN. The gases rise into the atmosphere and are carried by the wind; when it rains the gases dissolve in the rain, to form acids like sulphuric and nitric acid (Figure 6.2.3). These acids:

- Can cause direct damage to the leaves of plants.
- Can acidify rivers and lakes, killing plants and animals. Fish are particularly susceptible as their gills become coated with thick mucus. This prevents gas exchange and the fish die.
- Cause aluminium salts to go into solution. These are toxic to both plants and fish. They may run off into lakes and rivers, damaging the ecosystems there.

Oxides of nitrogen and CFCs

The ozone layer of the atmosphere is being destroyed by oxides of nitrogen and substances called CFCs (chlorofluorocarbons). CFCs are used as refrigerants and in aerosols and plastic foams. These gases react with ozone, reducing its concentration, and as a result more UV light reaches the Earth's surface. This:

- Increases the risk of skin cancer.
- Can damage plant crops.
- Can influence weather patterns.

NB Do not confuse the effect of ozone depletion with the increase in the greenhouse effect.

Air quality

Poor air quality due to accumulation of polluting gases, smoke and microscopic particles has been shown to cause asthma attacks and to increase the number of cases of respiratory disease, especially bronchitis. Particles of tar and carbon may increase the risk of cancer.

Carbon monoxide produced by fossil fuels can combine with haemoglobin forming CARBOXYHAEMOGLOBIN. This is a stable compound and therefore reduces the ability of haemoglobin to carry oxygen. This is particularly a problem for young children who live close to heavily used roads.

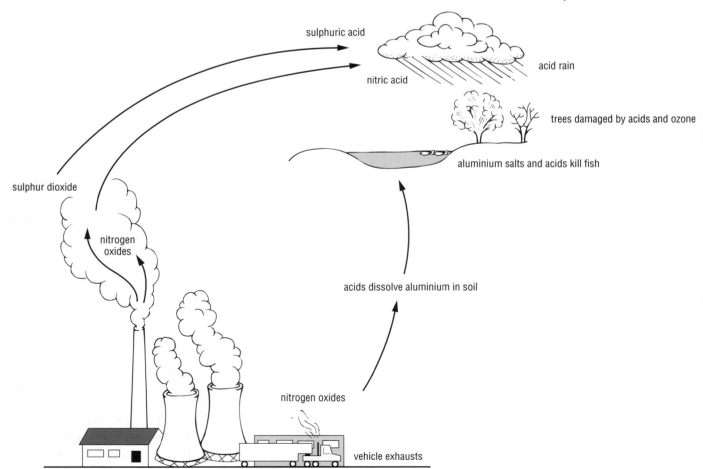

Figure 6.2.3 Acid rain formation

Industrial wastes

Toxic chemicals are produced by industrial processes. These include heavy metals such as lead (which is an enzyme inhibitor), mercury and cadmium. These chemicals can accumulate in the food chains, causing harm to animals and even humans.

Water is used as a cooling agent in many industrial processes. When discharged into rivers as warm water it tends to accelerate eutrophication, since enzymes become more active and respiration speeds up at higher temperatures.

Sewage

As the human population increases, so does the amount of sewage that must be treated. The effluent from a sewage treatment plant contains nitrates and phosphates. Again this will accelerate eutrophication since the salts accelerate the growth and multiplication of the microscopic floating algae.

Loss of land/ecosystems

As human populations increase, less land is available to other species. More and more land is used for:

- Building homes and factories.
- Quarrying, to obtain raw materials for industry.
- Agriculture, to try to keep up with food demands.
- Treating or dumping waste in, for example, landfill sites and toxic waste sites.

How can the environment be protected/conserved?

1 Increased use of renewable energy sources, such as wind power, hydroelectric power, ethanol-based fuels and biogas, would reduce the use of fossil fuels.
2 Recycling of materials would reduce the need for mining and quarrying. Aluminium, lead, copper, glass and paper are easily recycled.
3 Conservation areas can be established, and rare and endangered species preserved.
4 Farmers can be encouraged to set aside land so that it can revert to its wild state. This would encourage increased species diversity.
5 Careful management of ecosystems can allow efficient food production while minimising damage to ecosystems. This would include:

- Enforcing quotas on the fishing industry and a minimum size of fish taken.
- Increased use of organic fertilisers.
- Use of selective weedkillers and other pesticides.

- Use of biological pest control, in which pest species are controlled using their natural enemies such as predators, parasites and pathogens. For example, whitefly (which is a pest in greenhouses) can be controlled by a parasitic wasp which lays its eggs in the whitefly's larvae. Biological control can be cheaper than use of chemicals and does not harm the environment. Careful research must be carried out, however, to ensure that the introduction of the controlling species does not affect the ecosystem adversely.

6 Reforestation, particularly of mixed woodland, will increase species diversity of both animals and plant types.
7 The introduction of new species must be carefully controlled.
8 Polluting gas emissions can be reduced by switching from coal- to gas-powered power stations, and by the use of CATALYTIC CONVERTERS in motor vehicles.

Quick Questions

1 What are the two most important 'greenhouse gases'?
2 What is the 'greenhouse effect'?
3 Give two causes of the increase in the greenhouse effect.
4 Describe the effect of deforestation on:
  a) The soil;
  b) Weather patterns;
  c) Species diversity.
5 What is monoculture and what is its effect on the environment?
6 List three effects of the overuse of fertilisers.
7 Which gases cause acid rain?
8 What is the effect of acid rain on plants and animals?
9 Which gases cause destruction of the ozone layer?
10 Pesticides and toxic chemicals 'accumulate' in the food chain. What does this mean?
11 What process is accelerated in rivers by the discharge of warm water and sewage? Explain why.

6.3 Interdependence of living organisms

All living organisms need energy. This energy is released during respiration. The energy comes from chemical energy stored in food molecules like glucose. This energy originated in the Sun and was trapped by green plants during photosynthesis. It was then stored in substances like starch inside plant cells. Animal cells and fungi cannot make their own food molecules and must rely, directly or indirectly, on green plants for them.

Organisms must therefore depend on each other for food. It is possible to trace the energy and materials from one organism to the next in a food chain. There are several feeding or trophic levels in a food chain, which include:

1 PRODUCERS (green plants), produce organic food molecules by photosynthesis.
2 PRIMARY CONSUMERS (herbivores), which feed directly on green plants.
3 SECONDARY CONSUMERS (carnivores), which feed on herbivores.
4 TERTIARY CONSUMERS (top carnivores), which feed on other carnivores.
5 SAPROPHYTES (decomposers like certain bacteria and fungi), which feed on dead or decaying organic matter/remains of plants and animals.

Some animals feed at more than one trophic level. Omnivores, for example, feed on both animals and plants.

Here is an example of a food chain.

tree leaves → leaf-eating insect → frog   → grass snake
(producer)   (primary   (secondary   (tertiary
                consumer)   consumer)   consumer)

In nature consumers rarely depend on only one type of food. As a result food chains are interconnected at many points, forming a food web (Figure 6.3.1).

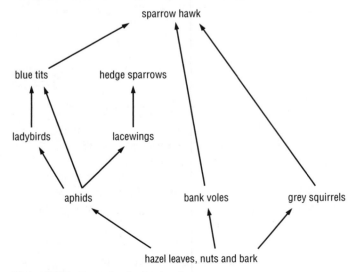

Figure 6.3.1 Example of a food web

Remember that the arrows in a food web represent the direction of movement (flow) of energy and materials.

If a member of a food web is lost, or its numbers fall dramatically, the whole web will be affected. Suppose that in the previous example the ladybird population fell, blue tits would lose one source of their food and would have to take more aphids. This would result in greater competition between blue tits and lacewings. As a result of lacewing numbers falling, the numbers of hedge sparrows would fall.

Pyramids of numbers

It is possible to study the numbers of organisms at each trophic level. Usually there are many small producers supporting fewer herbivores, which in turn support fewer (but larger) carnivores. This can be represented as a pyramid of numbers (Figure 6.3.2).

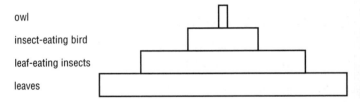

Figure 6.3.2 Example of a pyramid of numbers

The sizes of the drawn rectangles represent the number of organisms at each trophic level.

Pyramid of biomass

Figure 6.3.3 is a pyramid of numbers for hazel, aphid, ladybird and blue tit.

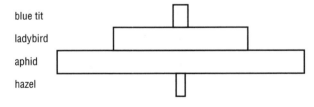

Figure 6.3.3 A pyramid of numbers for part of an ecosystem on a hazel tree

In this case the pyramid is not really a pyramid because there is only one producer. We can overcome this by constructing a pyramid of **biomass** (Figure 6.3.4). This is much more accurate, as it is a pyramid based on the actual dry mass of organisms at each trophic level. It takes into account, for example, that although there may be many thousands of aphids their individual dry mass is very small. So for the same food chain the pyramid of biomass would be in grams per square metre.

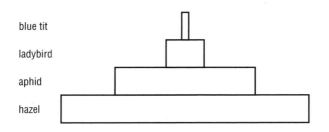

Figure 6.3.4 A pyramid of biomass

Pyramids of energy

It is possible to construct these by calculating the energy available at each trophic level per unit of area in a year. This would show progressively less energy available at each trophic level. The units here would be $kJ/m^2/year$.

Transfer of energy and materials

Pyramids of biomass and energy clearly show that there is a loss between each trophic level.

- Only about 1% of sunlight energy is used by plants in photosynthesis to make organic matter in their cells.
- Primary consumers do not eat all the vegetation, nor are they able to digest all they eat. Only that part of their food that they digest and absorb can be used by them to provide energy or to make new cells.
- Secondary and tertiary consumers do not eat all prey or all of a prey animal. Again, only a small proportion can be used by the animal for energy and the production of cells.
- At each trophic level, only the energy/materials that are used to make new cells is available to the next level.
- At each trophic level some of the materials are lost in waste materials such as urine, or in undigested waste like faeces.
- At each trophic level respiration takes place, releasing energy for living processes like cell division and muscle contraction. This energy is therefore not available to be passed on to the next level.
- Energy is lost as heat to the surroundings. These losses are greatest in endotherms like mammals and birds which maintain a constant body temperature.
- Uneaten vegetation and remnants of animal bodies will be used as a source of energy by decomposers. Once they have broken down the waste and dead bodies and recycled all the materials, all the energy originally trapped by green plants will have been transferred to the environment.

Increasing efficiency of food production

Humans feed at the end of food chains and must try to manage food production to reduce the amount of energy wasted. This is achieved by:

1 Reducing the number of stages in food chains; it is more energy-efficient to eat plant products like bread, pasta, soya protein and mycoprotein.
2 Managing natural ecosystems carefully – fish stocks in the North Sea, for example (see section 6.2).
3 Creating artificial ecosystems like fish farms, battery systems (for hens and pigs) and glasshouses for plant crops. Here food production is kept at high levels by:
   a) Providing optimum conditions like temperature and light intensity to ensure maximum yield.
   b) Providing optimum feeding conditions.
   c) In the case of animals, reducing energy loss by limiting living space. This restricts the animal's movements and therefore saves energy.
   d) Controlling disease and predation using pesticides, biological control and drugs.
   e) Using pesticides or biological control to prevent damage to crops and animals and to prevent loss in storage, as in cereal silos.

In using both natural and artificial ecosystems humans must compromise between their demand for food, the impact on the environment and their duty to treat animals as humanely as possible.

Nutrient cycles

Living things remove materials from their environment. In a stable community this must be balanced by processes that return materials. Recycling of materials depends on saprophytes or decomposers (Figures 6.3.5 and 6.3.6). These include bacteria and fungi which feed on and digest animal waste and dead plant and animal remains. Decomposition caused by microbes occurs faster:

- In warm conditions.
- In moist conditions.
- If there is plenty of oxygen (material must not be too compact, air must be allowed to move freely).

These conditions favour multiplication and activity of the microorganisms. Gardeners use compost heaps or compost makers to produce organic fertilisers. Grass cuttings and kitchen waste are also used.

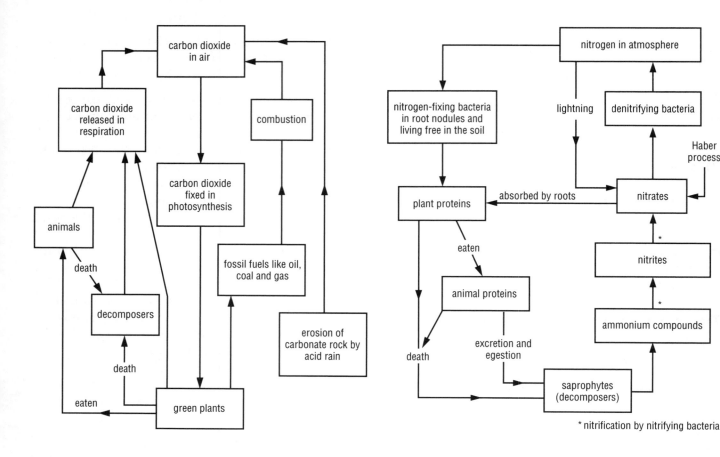

Figure 6.3.5 The carbon cycle

Figure 6.3.6 The nitrogen cycle

* nitrification by nitrifying bacteria

Role of microorganisms in the nitrogen cycle

Saprophytes (decomposers)

Bacteria and fungi decompose animal waste and plant and animal remains, producing ammonium compounds. Examples include:

- NITRIFYING BACTERIA – the production of nitrate from ammonium compounds occurs in two steps:

  1 Nitrite bacteria convert ammonium compounds to nitrite.
  2 Nitrite bacteria convert nitrite into nitrate.

- DENITRIFYING BACTERIA – these break down nitrates in the soil into nitrogen gas.

- NITROGEN-FIXING BACTERIA – these are found in swellings on the roots of leguminous plants like pea and bean plants. They have a symbiotic relationship with the plant (see section 3.1). They are able to convert nitrogen in the air between soil particles into ammonium compounds which the plants can use, thus allowing them to flourish in poor soils.

Quick Questions

1 All food webs/chains start with a green plant. Why?
2 What are saprophytes?
3 What is the food of
   a) Primary consumers?
   b) Secondary consumers?
4 What does an omnivore feed on?
5 What do the arrows in a food chain/web represent?
6 In a typical food chain, as you move from one trophic level to the next what happens to the number and size of the organisms?
7 Give two ways in which materials/energy are lost in moving from one trophic level to the next.
8 Give two ways in which food production is kept at high levels in an artificial ecosystem.
9 What are the best conditions for decomposition in a compost heap?
10 What processes release carbon dioxide into the atmosphere?
11 What process removes carbon dioxide from the atmosphere?
12 What are the roles in the nitrogen cycle of:
   a) Nitrifying bacteria?
   b) Saprophytes?
   c) Nitrogen-fixing bacteria?

Section Six: Examination Questions

1. The drawings show the heads of four birds, not drawn to scale. The birds feed in different ways.

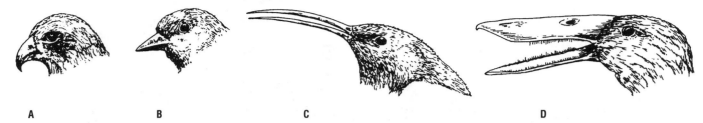

A   B   C   D

Which of the birds, **A**, **B**, **C** or **D**, is best adapted for

(a) Tearing flesh?

(b) Finding insects in cracks in the ground?

(c) Crushing fruit?

(d) Sieving small animals from mud?   [4]

(NEAB, Tier I, June 1997)

2. The table below shows birth rates and death rates for some countries.

Country	Annual birth rate per 1000 population	Annual death rate per 1000 population
China	20	8
USA	15	9
India	34	15
Britain	12	12
Sweden	12	11

(a) (i)   Which country shows the greatest annual rate of increase in its population?   [1]

     (ii)   Which country shows **no** annual increase in its population?   [1]

     (iii) Which country shows the smallest annual rate of increase in its population?   [1]

(b) Give **two** major problems faced by a country with a large increase in its population.   [2]

(SEG, Foundation, Specimen)

3. The drawings show changes to a farm between 1953 and 1983.

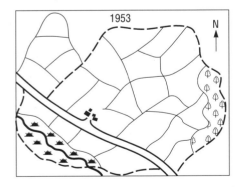 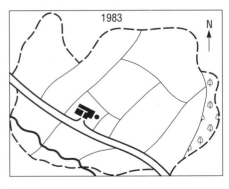 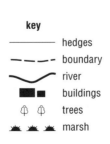

key
——— hedges
– – – boundary
～ river
■ ■ buildings
♁ ♁ trees
⁕ ⁕ ⁕ marsh

The fields on the farm are separated by hedges.

(a) (i)   Give **two** major changes which were made to the land on this farm between 1953 and 1983. [2]

     (ii) How would these changes affect the number of wild animals which live on the farmland? Explain your answer.   [2]

(b) The farm is an 'organic farm'. The waste products from the cows are spread on the fields.

     (i)   Describe, in as much detail as possible, what happens to the nitrogen compounds in these waste products after they have been spread on the fields.   [4]

     (ii) Explain why spreading animal waste on the fields may increase the farmer's income.   [1]

(c) In this country the use of non-biodegradable pesticides is now banned. Explain why.   [2]

(NEAB Coordinated Science, June 1997)

4. The diagram shows the mass of carbon involved each year in some of the processes in the carbon cycle.

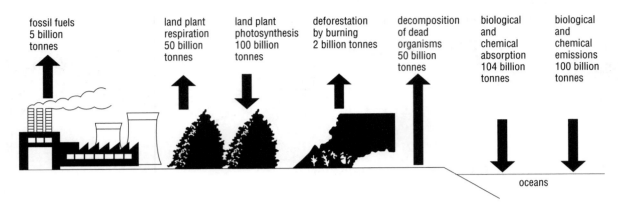

(a) Complete the equation for plant respiration.

.... + oxygen → carbon dioxide + ... + energy   [2]

(b) **(i)** Calculate the mass of carbon removed from the atmosphere each year. Show your working.   [1]
    (ii) Calculate the percentage of this total which is removed by the photosynthesis of land plants. Show your working.   [2]

(c) Power stations often discharge warm water into rivers. Describe how this warm water might affect organisms which live in the river.   [3]

(d) The worldwide use of fossil fuels has increased rapidly during this century.
    (i) Give **two** reasons for the increase in the amount of fossil fuels used.   [2]
    (ii) Give **two** effects on the environment of this increase in the amount of fossil fuels used.   [2]
    (iii) Describe and explain the long-term effects of large-scale deforestation on the Earth's atmosphere.   [4]

(e) Give **two** reasons why the proportion of methane in the atmosphere is rising.   [2]

(NEAB, Tier R, June 1995)

5. Read the following newspaper article.

Seal death horror

Pollution blamed

Reports have been coming in from the east coast of hundreds of dead seals being washed up or found dying at sea. The seals appear to have died from a type of flu. Scientists think that the seals' immune system may have been damaged by chemicals polluting their food.

    The local fishing crews are said to be pleased because their catches of cod have increased. Their spokesperson said: 'Less seals eat fewer cod so there are more for us.' With the summer weather causing rapid growth of tiny plants called plankton, the numbers of small fish on which the cod feed are also increasing.

(a) Explain why flu was killing so many seals when normally most would have survived this disease. [2]

(b) Fill in the boxes to show the food chain described in the newspaper article.

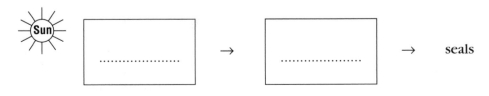

[2]

(continued)

Scientists have been studying a number of pollutants now being found in the sea. A report card on the group of chemicals called PCBs is shown below.

PCB REPORT CARD

Features of chemical:
Does not dissolve in water;
Can dissolve in fats/oils;
Excellent electrical insulator;
Very stable chemical, does not easily break down.

Used in the manufacture of:
Paints;
Electrical equipment;
Flame proofing.

   (c) Seals are mammals and so feed their young on milk. PCB pollution kills more baby seals than adult seals. Use the information from the report card to explain this.   [3]

                                                                 (MEG (Salters), Higher, Specimen)

6. Last year, half a million tonnes of detergents were flushed into rivers in Britain. Most detergents contain phosphates, which prevent the formation of scum on clothes. Some detergents contain enzymes. The use of phosphates in detergents is banned in Switzerland and Holland because cadmium is a by-product of phosphate production. This could reach water supplies. There are no controls in Britain despite this hazard of the heavy metal.

    A substance called zeolite can be used instead of phosphate and has no side effects. When phosphates enter water, they can be used by algae and act as a fertiliser. Rivers and lakes can become 'over-fertile' and cause a dense blanket of growth of algae on the surface of the river.

    The composition of some detergents and information about their manufacture is shown in the following table:

Name	North Sea oil used in manufacture	Phosphate present	Enzymes present	Plant oils used in manufacture
Ariel	+	+	+	−
Bold	+	+	+	−
Ecover	−	−	−	+
Daz	+	+	+	−
Lux	−	−	−	−
Persil	−	+	+	−
Asda Auto	+	−	−	−
Tesco Auto	+	−	+	−

Key + = yes − = no

   (a) Name **one** detergent which would be banned in Holland.   [1]
   (b) (i)   Name **one** detergent which would be successful in boiling water.   [1]
         (ii) Explain your answer to (i).   [2]
   (c) Explain why the process of producing phosphate could be harmful to the environment.   [3]
   (d) Explain how a dense blanket of floating algae might affect the environment where the algae live. [3]
   (e) If you were a detergent manufacturer, explain how you would avoid environmental pollution and still prevent the formation of scum on clothes.   [1]
   (f) As a result of similar pollution of the Adriatic Sea, large numbers of algae flourish and cause a problem for the tourist industry.

      German scientists have discovered a virus which attacks and kills a type of freshwater algae called *Chlorella*.
      (i)   If a biologist suggested the use of this virus to solve the problem in the Adriatic Sea, what major assumption would she be making?
      (ii) Why would environmentalists be worried about introducing the virus to the Adriatic Sea?   [2]

                                                                  (WJEC, Higher, Specimen)

---

7. A fish farm is a managed ecosystem. The diagram below represents a salmon farm on a Scottish loch and shows some of the other organisms living in the area.

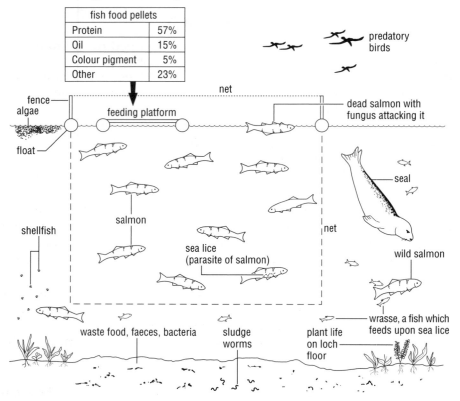

fish food pellets	
Protein	57%
Oil	15%
Colour pigment	5%
Other	23%

(a) Use the diagram to suggest how the fish farm maximises its production. [3]

(b) Suggest **two** methods for removing the sea lice which damage the salmon's skin. [2]

(c) The salmon are fed five times per day in small quantities rather than in one large amount. What effect would this have on the oxygen content of the water? Explain your answer. [3]

(d) What effects could the salmon farm have on the environment, including the populations of other organisms in the area? [4]

(London, Higher, Specimen)

8. An oak wood contained the following:

200 oak trees
150 000 primary consumers
120 000 secondary consumers

(a) Draw and label a pyramid of biomass for this wood. (Your pyramid does **not** have to be drawn to scale.) [2]

(b) A scientist estimated the total amount of energy flow through each level of the pyramid per year. The results were:

Energy absorbed by oak trees	4 600 000 kJ per m^2 per year
Energy in sugar produced by trees	44 000 kJ per m^2 per year
Energy transferred to primary consumers	2 920 kJ per m^2 per year
Energy transferred to secondary consumers	700 kJ per m^2 per year

(i) Calculate the percentage of the energy absorbed by the trees that is transferred to sugar by photosynthesis. Show your working. [2]

(ii) Suggest **two** reasons why a large proportion of the energy is not transferred to sugar. [2]

(iii) Give **three** reasons why some of the energy in the primary consumers is **not** passed on to the secondary consumers. [3]

(c) In autumn, the leaves fall from the oak trees. The leaves contain some proteins.
    Explain how the nitrogen in these proteins is made available for the oak trees to use again. [4]

(NEAB, Tier R, June 1996)

9. A group of students studied the feeding pattern in a pond. The food web below shows their results.

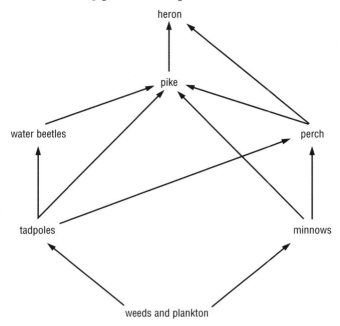

(a) Explain why there are likely to be fewer pike than plankton in the pond. [2]

(b) A disease killed most of the minnows. Describe and explain the likely effects of this on the other organisms at the **same** trophic level in the pond. [3]

(c) Inorganic fertiliser from a local farm drained into the pond. Describe and explain the effects that this could have on the organisms in the pond. [5]

(SEG, Higher, Specimen)

10. The diagram shows part of the nitrogen cycle.

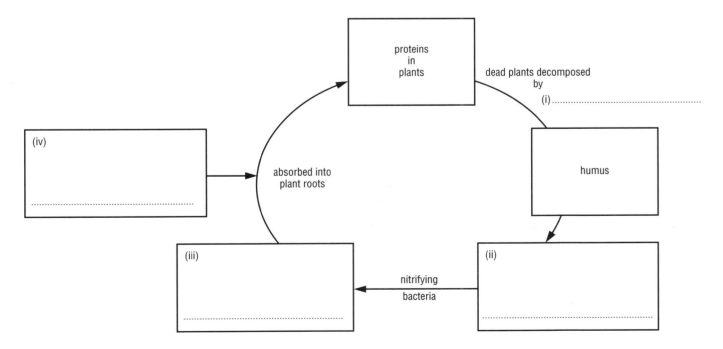

(a) Complete the diagram by filling in parts (i) to (iv). [4]

(b) Plants may be eaten by animals. The nitrogen in the proteins eaten may eventually be returned to the environment in compounds which can be used by other plants. Give **two** ways in which this happens. [2]

(continued)

Nitrogen-fixing bacteria can grow in clover plants. As the bacteria grow they form small lumps, called nodules. Clover seeds may be sprayed with nitrogen-fixing bacteria before farmers sow them.

In an investigation clover seeds were planted in two pots. The seeds planted in pot A were sterilised. The seeds planted in pot B were sprayed with nitrogen-fixing bacteria. A clover plant from each pot is shown in the drawing below.

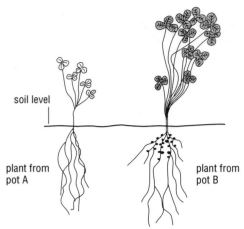

(c) (i) What evidence is there from this investigation that spraying the clover seeds with nitrogen-fixing bacteria is useful? [2]

(ii) Farmers may plant clover and then plough it into the soil before planting a cereal crop. Explain how this would make the soil more fertile. [2]

(d) Nitrogen-fixing bacteria have genes which enable them to fix nitrogen. These bacteria will not grow in cereal crops such as wheat. How might it benefit the environment if farmers could grow cereal crops which fix nitrogen?

(NEAB, Level Q, June 1994)

11. The diagram shows a food web for some of the organisms which live in a pond.

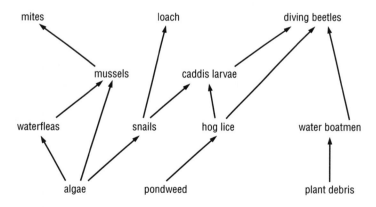

(a) Name **one** secondary consumer in this food web. [1]

(b) This is a pyramid of biomass for the organisms in the pond.

Some of the biomass of the producers is **not** transferred to the tertiary consumers. Explain as fully as you can what happens to this biomass. [6]

(NEAB, Level R, June 1995)

Section SEVEN

Microorganisms, their characteristics and use

7.1 Types of microorganism

Viruses

Viruses are not living organisms, strictly speaking, since they do not have cell components such as mitochondria and they cannot reproduce/multiply by themselves. Examples include polio and 'cold' virus.

Viruses are extremely small and because of this their structure is simple. They have a protein 'coat' which surrounds genetic material, which may be either DNA or RNA. There is no cytoplasm (Figure 7.1.1).

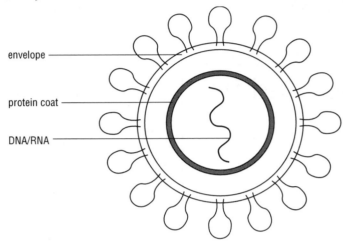

actual diameter = approx. 0.2 μm

Figure 7.1.1 The structure of a virus

Stages of virus reproduction
- The virus attaches to the host cell surface.
- The genetic material of the virus is inserted into the host cell.
- The genetic material of the virus multiplies.
- The viral genetic material takes over the host cell.
- The host cell starts to manufacture virus genetic material and protein coat.
- Newly formed virus particles are released from the host cell as it bursts.

Bacteria

These are larger and more complex than viruses and show all the characteristics of living organisms. They carry out all the life processes (see section 1.1). They do not have a nucleus, and their genetic material, a chromosome, is free in the cytoplasm. They have a cell membrane and a cell wall, which is not made of cellulose (see Figure 5.4.1 on page 94). In addition bacteria may have a protective outer coat and sometimes a flagellum. Although most bacteria are not harmful to humans, examples include *Salmonella* and *Escherichia coli* (*E. coli*). Bacteria are divided into different groups depending on their shape/form (Figure 7.1.2).

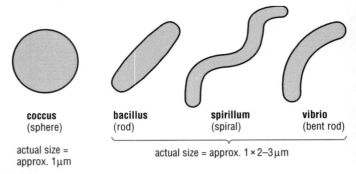

| **coccus** (sphere) | **bacillus** (rod) | **spirillum** (spiral) | **vibrio** (bent rod) |

actual size = approx. 1μm

actual size = approx. 1 × 2–3 μm

Figure 7.1.2 Types of bacteria

Bacteria reproduce asexually by BINARY FISSION – division of nuclear material and the cytoplasm. This produces two identical daughter cells. They may also produce hard-coated reproductive spores which can resist drought, extremes of temperature and some poisons. In spore form they can survive for many years.

Fungi

YEASTS: these are single-celled organisms and have a nucleus, cytoplasm, cell membrane and cell wall (Figure 7.1.3). They reproduce by BINARY FISSION, sometimes called budding. They are important in industry because they carry out FERMENTATION (see section 7.2).

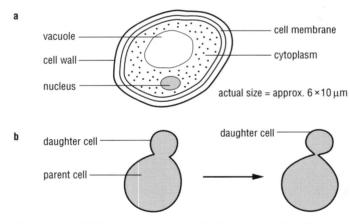

a

vacuole — cell membrane

cell wall — cytoplasm

nucleus

actual size = approx. 6 × 10 μm

b

daughter cell

daughter cell

parent cell

Figure 7.1.3 (**a**) Structure of a yeast cell; (**b**) a yeast cell budding

MOULDS: these fungi have thread-like structures called HYPHAE which grow on or through their food source. They carry out extracellular digestion, releasing enzymes on to the food and absorbing the digested products.

The hyphae have cytoplasm with many nuclei surrounded by a cell wall. The feeding hyphae or main body of the fungus (MYCELIUM) produces SPORANGIA which gives rise to spores by asexual reproduction (see Figure 5.4.3 on page 94).

Single-celled algae

These organisms have cells that have a nucleus, cytoplasm, chloroplasts, a cell membrane and a cellulose cell wall (Figure 7.1.4).

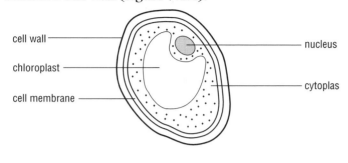

actual size = approx.12 × 20 µm

Figure 7.1.4 A single-celled alga

Growing or culturing microbes

Microbes are grown in the laboratory in a **culture medium** which contains carbohydrate as an energy source, mineral ions and in some cases supplements such as vitamins or protein extracts. A special ASEPTIC TECHNIQUE is used to grow uncontaminated cultures of microbes.

Aseptic technique

In order to prepare useful products, uncontaminated cultures of microbes are required. Petri dishes and growth media should be sterilised before use to kill unwanted microbes. Precautions must be taken to prevent contamination when pouring sterile growth media into sterile Petri dishes. An inoculating loop is used first to scoop up and transfer a small piece of the colony of microbes to a growth medium, and then to make a 'zig-zag' streak on the surface of the growth medium. The loop is sterilised before and after use by passing it through a Bunsen burner flame (Figure 7.1.5).

The lid of a Petri dish prevents microbes from the air from contaminating a culture and should be kept on whenever possible. After the inoculations, the Petri dish should be sealed with adhesive tape.

In school laboratories, cultures should be incubated at a maximum temperature of 25 °C to discourage growth of microbes that could be harmful to humans. After use, cultures should be destroyed safely by using strong disinfectant or high temperatures.

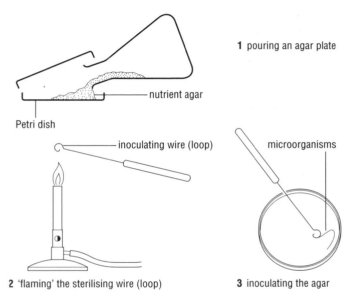

1 pouring an agar plate

nutrient agar

Petri dish

inoculating wire (loop)

microorganisms

2 'flaming' the sterilising wire (loop)

3 inoculating the agar

Figure 7.1.5 Setting up a culture of microorganisms

Quick Questions

1 Put a tick in the correct boxes in the table to show which structures are found in the organisms listed.

	Cytoplasm	Nucleus	Chloroplast	Cellulose cell wall
Viruses				
Bacteria				
Yeasts				
Moulds				
Algae				

2 What must a culture medium contain?

3 Why must equipment such as Petri dishes and inoculating loops be sterile if you want to create cultures of microorganisms?

4 Why should cultures be incubated at only 25 °C in school labs?

5 How do bacteria and yeasts reproduce?

6 How do moulds reproduce?

7 What is the name of the thread-like structures of moulds that grow on or through their food?

7.2 Microbes and industry

Microbes are used in many industrial processes, often involving the process known as fermentation. This is any process during which organisms use an external food source to obtain energy. They chemically change the medium in which they are growing.

Production of yoghurt

- Milk is heated to between 85 °C and 95 °C for 15–30 minutes; this will kill any pathogenic bacteria in the milk.
- The milk is cooled to between 45 °C and 35 °C.
- A starter culture of *LACTOBACILLUS* BACTERIA is added and the mixture incubated at 40 °C for 8 hours.
- The bacteria ferment the milk sugar (lactose), producing lactic acid.
- The lactic acid causes the milk protein to become solid.

Production of cheese

- The milk is heat-treated to kill bacteria.
- The milk is cooled and a starter culture is added. The culture is usually a mixture of *Streptococcus* bacteria.
- After 24 hours at 18 °C the lactic acid produced has coagulated the milk into curds (solid) and whey (liquid).
- Curds and whey are separated and the curds are put into stainless steel or wooden drums.
- They are pressed and allowed to dry.
- The 'cheese' may then be infected with fungi to produce different flavours, such as blue Stilton.

Production of mycoprotein

This is sometimes called single-cell protein, and is marketed as a meat substitute under the name Quorn.

Mycoprotein is produced today by a continuous fermentation process. The culture medium is carbohydrate, which can be obtained from various cheap or waste materials such as molasses, potato starch or sugar beet. The species normally cultured is called *Fusarium*. It is the mycelium of the fungus which is harvested as mycoprotein.

The fungus is cultured in large fermenters (Figure 7.2.1). Conditions in the fermenter are carefully controlled to ensure high productivity with good mycelial growth. Most fermenters have the following features:

- A water-cooled jacket to remove heat produced by the respiring microbes.
- Aseptic conditions.
- A stirring device or agitator to ensure even distribution of nutrients in the fermenter.

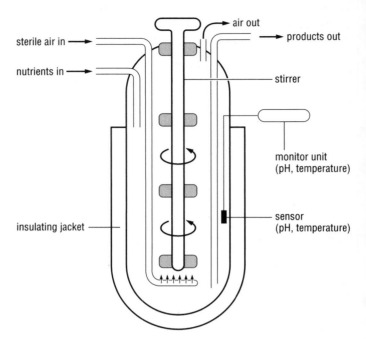

Figure 7.2.1 A diagram of a fermenter

- A supply of sterile air to provide oxygen for the microbes.
- Devices for monitoring pH, temperature, nutrient and product concentrations.

The fungus grows in the fermenter for several weeks and afterwards is separated from the culture medium and washed in steam. The so-called 'filter cake' of mycoprotein is then quickly frozen or dried before it is processed into food products.

Mycoprotein is an excellent form of food protein, and there are several advantages in growing these microorganisms to provide food.

- The mycoprotein is low in cholesterol.
- Microorganisms grow very rapidly.
- They can use waste products from other industrial processes and cheap low-grade food.
- They are easy to handle and grow.
- Many crops can grow only in warm climates or in certain seasons. Mycoprotein can be produced anywhere all year round.
- The product is always of the same quality.
- The processing plant requires very little land area.

Yeast and the brewing and baking industry

Yeasts use glucose as a source of energy and their enzymes break it down in the absence of oxygen (anaerobically), producing ethanol and carbon dioxide:

glucose → ethanol + carbon dioxide + energy

The rate at which the yeast respires and therefore grows is affected by:

- Temperature.
- How much glucose is available.
- The build-up of alcohol, which is toxic to yeast cells.

Even at optimum temperatures, the rate of anaerobic respiration and yeast cell multiplication will eventually slow down and stop. This is because the glucose runs out and the level of ethanol rises. Temperatures above the optimum will denature the yeast enzymes.

Brewing

Cereals like oats are used in the brewing of beer. The starch in the grain is broken down by the enzyme amylase (from the yeast) to glucose, which it then ferments. In winemaking the grapes or other fruits provide the sugar for the yeast to work on.

Beer and wine can easily be made at home using home fermentation kits. The air lock in the top of the fermentation vessel allows carbon dioxide to escape, so pressure doesn't build up. It also prevents the entry of air which may contain bacteria as well as oxygen (see Examination question 6).

Baking

In baking:

- A mixture of sugar and yeast is mixed with bread dough (flour and water).
- This mixture is left in a warm place.
- As the yeast respires, carbon dioxide is produced which makes the bread 'rise'.
- The bread is then baked in a hot oven which evaporates any ethanol.

Production of soy sauce

Soy sauce is made from cooked soy beans and roasted wheat.

- Soy beans are soaked and cooked and then formed into a pulp.
- To the pulp is added crushed roasted wheat, together with a starter culture of moist soy flour, wheat bran and the fungus *Aspergillus*.
- The mixture is spread into thin layers and kept at 25–35 °C for 2 days (the fungus turns the mixture green).
- The mixture is then fermented in large vessels for up to 4 months. Other yeasts and lactobacilli are added at this stage.
- The product of this fermentation is filtered and pasteurised (heated to 70 °C).
- The pasteurised sauce is put into sterile bottles.

Use of microbes to make antibiotics

Many antibiotics are now manufactured using microorganisms. Penicillin is made by growing the mould *Penicillium* in fermenters (Figure 7.2.2).

- A starter culture of *Pencillium* is added to a liquid culture medium in a large fermenter.
- The cells multiply rapidly and the sugar concentration of the medium falls.
- As sugar concentration falls antibiotic production increases.
- After 7 days the medium is filtered and the penicillin extracted. The waste medium can be used to make animal feed.
- The filtered penicillin solution is evaporated.

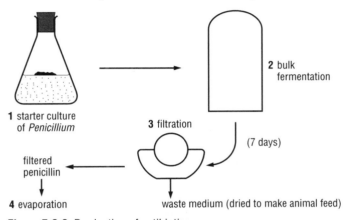

1 starter culture of *Penicillium*
2 bulk fermentation
3 filtration
(7 days)
filtered penicillin
4 evaporation
waste medium (dried to make animal feed)

Figure 7.2.2 Production of antibiotics

Use of microbes to produce fuels

Fuels can be made from natural products by fermentation processes. This provides an alternative fuel to fossil fuels and at the same time makes use of waste materials.

Ethanol-based fuels

These can be made as a result of anaerobic respiration carried out by yeasts on either sugar cane juice, or glucose produced from maize starch. The maize starch is broken down by amylases to produce the glucose.

The products of the fermentation process are then distilled and the ethanol can then be used as fuel for motor vehicles.

Biogas

This is mainly METHANE produced by anaerobic fermentation. A wide range of organic waste materials can be fermented by METHANOGENIC BACTERIA to produce methane.

Biogas generators of various designs can be used. Figure 7.2.3 shows one design. For efficient biogas production:

- The generator must be gas-tight to maintain anaerobic conditions.

- There must be a way of introducing new waste and removing digested waste without losing gas.
- There must be mixing of new and old waste to ensure the methanogenic bacteria are passed on.
- The temperature must be kept at around 15 °C for fermentation to occur. This means that they must be insulated or even heated, especially in winter. Some of the biogas produced can be used as fuel in a generator.

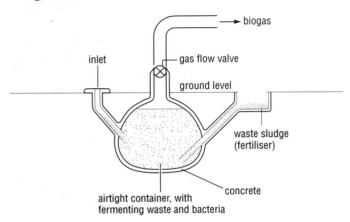

Figure 7.2.3 A biogas generator

Biogas can be produced on a small scale, particularly on farms. Animal faeces can be used in a generator to provide energy – to heat farm buildings, for instance. On a larger scale waste from sugar factories could be used to provide energy for a small community. The sludge left at the end of sewage treatment can be put into sealed tanks, where it will be digested to form methane. This can then be used as a fuel for the sewage works. Landfill sites are also a source of biogas; it is collected by sinking pipes deep into the waste and then pumping out the gas.

Microorganisms as a source of enzymes

Enzymes are of great value in industry because they bring about reactions at normal temperatures and pressures. Without enzymes, very expensive energy-demanding equipment would be required.

Many industrial enzymes are now produced by microorganisms. This is because:

- They multiply very rapidly.
- They are easy to grow and have simple food requirements. Often they can be grown on cheap waste materials.
- They can be genetically engineered to produce new enzymes; an example is lipase for detergents.

Industrial enzymes are very robust and can withstand a wide range of working conditions. For example, they can continue to work over wide temperature and pH ranges and for long periods of time.

Industrial enzymes are stabilised and protected by immobilising them in an inert (non-reactive) support carrier. This can be ALGINATE BEADS, an INERT MATRIX or HOLLOW FIBRES.

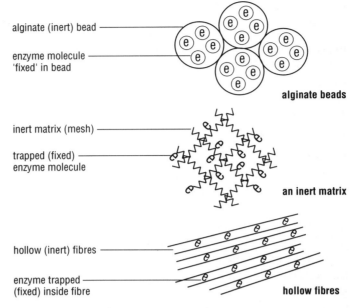

Figure 7.2.4 Enzyme supports (e = enzyme)

Immobilised enzymes have many advantages:

- The enzyme can always be fully recovered.
- The product is not contaminated by the enzyme.
- The enzyme's activity can be confined and more easily controlled.
- The enzyme is more stable.
- They allow continuous production instead of batch production. (In batch processing the enzyme is mixed with substrate and allowed to react; then product and enzyme must be removed from the reaction vessel and separated.)

Enzymes are involved in the following:

1 Biological detergents contain proteases and lipases.
2 Proteases are used to predigest the protein in baby food.
3 Pectinases are used to extract fruit juice from fruit pulp.
4 Carbohydrases are used to change starch into sugar syrup.
5 Isomerases are used to convert glucose syrup into fructose syrup. This is sweeter, so it is useful in slimming foods since less needs to be used.
6 The enzyme catalase and its substrate hydrogen peroxide have been used in wound dressings. The catalase releases oxygen from the peroxide, providing an oxygen-rich environment. This promotes rapid healing and prevents infection by anaerobic bacteria, including those that cause gangrene.

The use of microbes in sewage treatment

Sewage contains organic material which must be broken down before the water can be released into rivers (see discussion of eutrophication in section 6.2). The organic matter is removed/digested by fermentation carried out by bacteria. There are two types of sewage treatment: the use of BIOLOGICAL FILTRATION and the newer system of ACTIVATED SLUDGE (Figure 7.2.5). Both systems use anaerobic bacteria in sludge digesters to produce methane.

Stages of sewage treatment

Preliminary treatment: incoming sewage passes through a screen which removes solid objects such as toilet paper or stones, and then passes through a grit-removing pit.

Sedimentation: the sewage flows into large settlement tanks, where solid suspended organic matter settles out to form a 'sludge' which is removed and pumped to the anaerobic digesters.

(i) *Biological filter method*: the liquid from the settlement tank is sprinkled over filter beds. These contain stones coated with aerobic bacteria. In the presence of oxygen the bacteria feed on the organic matter, both solid and dissolved, producing carbon dioxide, water and ammonium salts.

(ii) *Activated sludge*: this is an alternative form to biological filtration. The liquid from the settlement tanks (see below) is pumped, along with some of the sludge containing bacteria and protozoa into aeration tanks. These tanks provide aerobic conditions as oxygen is added either by mechanical agitation or by pumping in air. The microorganisms digest suspended organic solids and absorb dissolved organic molecules. Again carbon dioxide, water and ammonium salts are produced.

Secondary settlements: here a sludge containing microorganisms settles out. This sludge is called activated sludge and some of it is recycled into aeration tanks. At this stage the effluent should contain very little organic matter. It will contain ammonium salts, nitrates and dissolved oxygen. This will stimulate algal growth in rivers (see section 6.2).

Anaerobic digesters: sludge removed from the sedimentation tanks is put into anaerobic tanks where anaerobic bacteria digest it, producing methane. The methane (biogas) produced is often used as a fuel in the sewage works. The sludge left at the end of this stage can be dried and used as fertiliser, providing it is free of pathogenic organisms.

Quick Questions

1 In yoghurt production, what does the starter culture contain?
2 In the production of both yoghurt and cheese the milk is first heated. Why?
3 What is mycoprotein?
4 Give two advantages of mycoprotein as a source of food.
5 What are the products of anaerobic respiration of glucose by yeasts?
6 What are the raw materials of soy sauce production?
7 What are the raw materials for ethanol-based fuels?
8 What is biogas?
9 Why are microorganisms such a useful source of enzymes for industry?
10 How are enzymes immobilised?
11 Give two industrial uses of enzymes extracted from microorganisms.
12 What happens in each of the following steps of the treatment of sewage?
    a) Preliminary treatment;
    b) Sedimentation;
    c) Activated sludge/aeration tanks;
    d) Anaerobic tanks/digesters.

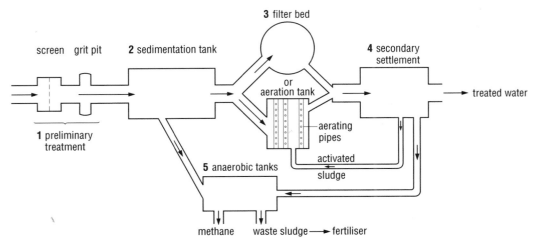

Figure 7.2.5 Sewage treatment plant

Section Seven: Examination Questions

1. (a) The diagram shows a virus.

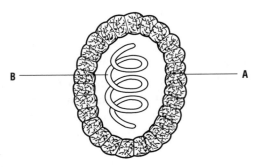

     (i)   What chemical substance is **A** made of?   [1]
     (ii) What chemical substance is **B** made of?   [1]
     (iii) Where do viruses reproduce?   [1]

(b) The diagram shows a bacterium.

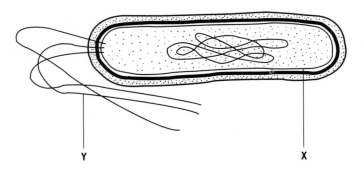

     (i)   Label the parts **X** and **Y**.   [2]
     (ii) Bacteria are difficult to destroy. Explain why.   [2]

                                                   (SEG, Higher, Specimen)

2. The diagram shows a bottle containing a stock culture of bacteria and a Petri dish containing nutrient jelly.

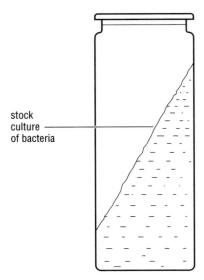

stock
culture
of bacteria

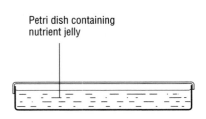

Petri dish containing
nutrient jelly

  (a) Describe how you would safely transfer bacteria from the stock culture to the nutrient jelly in the Petri dish.   [3]
  (b) Nutrient jelly containing only two food substances can be used to grow many types of bacteria. What are these two food substances?   [2]

                                                   (NEAB, Tier F, Specimen)

3. (a) The flow diagram below shows the stages in making yoghurt.

Heat milk slowly to boiling point
↓
Allow to cool
↓
Add the bacterial starter to the milk
↓
Pour the mixture into containers which have been
thoroughly cleaned and rinsed with very hot water
↓
Incubate the mixture of milk and starter for about 8 hours at 40 °C
↓
Once the yoghurt has set, place it in a refrigerator

Use the flow diagram and your own knowledge to answer the following questions.
- (i) Give **two** ways in which bacteria, apart from those in the starter, are prevented from growing in the milk. [2]
- (ii) Why is the milk cooled before the starter is added? [1]

(b) Describe what happens to the bacteria in the starter after they are added to the warm milk and explain how the bacteria help in yoghurt production. [4]

(London, Foundation, Specimen)

4. Mycoprotein, which is made from a fungus called *Fusarium*, is used as food for humans. The table below shows the main nutritional differences between mycoprotein and beef.

Nutrient	Nutrients in mycoprotein and beef (percentage of dry mass)	
	Mycoprotein	Beef
Protein	40–45	60–65
Fat	10–15	30–40
Mineral salts	3–4	1–2
Fibre	30–40	0

(a) Suggest **two** reasons why mycoprotein would be more suitable than beef as part of a healthy diet. [2]
(b) Explain the advantages of growing microorganisms for food compared with using crop plants or farm animals. [4]

(London, Higher, Specimen)

5. The diagram shows the preparation of a Petri dish containing agar jelly on which a culture of bacteria is to be grown.

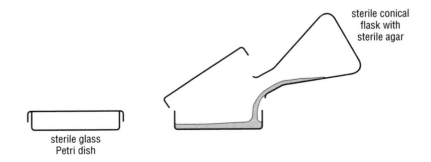

sterile conical
flask with
sterile agar

sterile glass
Petri dish

(a) How should the flask and agar be sterilised? [1]
(b) Why is it necessary to use a sterile Petri dish? [1]
(c) How should you introduce bacteria into the Petri dish? [2]

(SEG, Higher, Specimen)

6. The ancient Egyptians made wine by crushing grapes and fermenting the juice they collected from them. Organisms like the one shown in the diagram grew on the skin of the grapes and their anaerobic respiration turned the grape juice into wine.

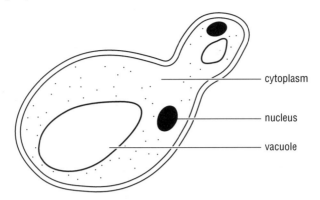

(a) (i)   How do you know that this organism is a fungus and not a bacterium? [1]
    (ii) What is meant by the word anaerobic? [1]
    (iii) Write a word equation to show how the sugar in grape juice is broken down by anaerobic respiration. [2]

(b) The diagram shows an apparatus which could be used to make wine at home.

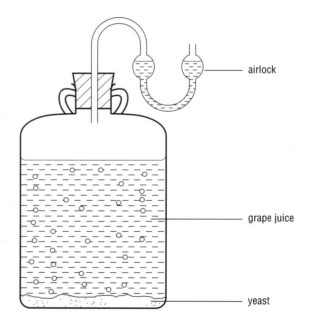

    (i)   What would happen to pressure inside the jar as fermentation proceeds? [1]
    (ii) What is the purpose of the airlock? [1]
    (iii) What might happen if a lot of air was allowed to enter the jar? [2]
    (iv) Why must the apparatus be carefully sterilised between each use? [1]

(c) Name the group of chemicals which bring about fermentation in the yeast. [1]

(MEG (Salters), Higher, Specimen)

7. A student investigated the effect of temperature on the production of carbon dioxide by yeast cells in a glucose solution. The diagram shows the apparatus she used.

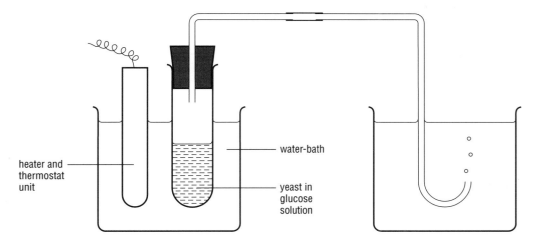

The student counted the number of bubbles produced in one minute with the water-bath temperature of 15 °C. She counted the bubbles for another minute and wrote down the mean of the two counts.

She increased the water-bath temperature by 5 °C and waited for 5 minutes after the water had reached the new temperature. She then counted the bubbles produced during another two periods and recorded the mean. This was repeated at higher temperatures. Her results are shown in the graph below.

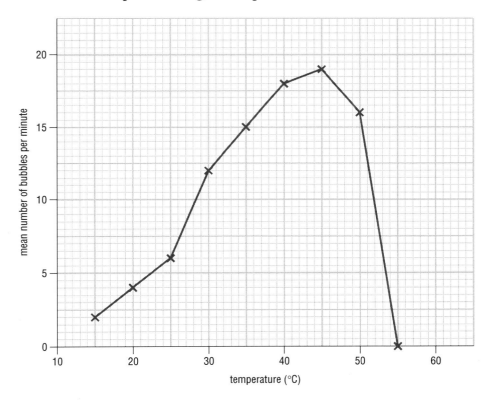

(a) (i) How many bubbles were produced per minute at 15 °C? [1]
    (ii) What was the effect, on the rate of bubbling, of increasing the temperature from 15 °C to 30 °C? [2]

(b) What was the effect, on the rate of bubbling, of increasing the temperature from 50 °C to 55 °C? Explain why this happened. [4]

(c) (i) Why did the student wait for 5 minutes after the water reached each new temperature, before counting the bubbles? [1]
    (ii) Why did she work out the mean of two counts at each temperature? [1]
    (iii) Suggest **one** way of making her investigation into a controlled experiment (fair test). [1]

(London, Foundation, Specimen)

8. A large dairy farm has the problem of disposing of large amounts of waste products from the cows. The farmer decides to install a biogas generator. This will dispose of the waste products and produce a useful fuel gas for the farm.

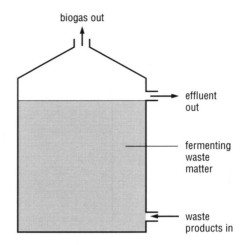

biogas out

effluent out

fermenting waste matter

waste products in

(a) The diagram shows a section through the farmer's generator.
  (i)   Name the fuel gas present in biogas. [1]
  (ii) What process in bacteria produces biogas? [1]
  (iii) Suggest **one** use for the biogas on the farm. [1]
(b) The farmer notices that the breakdown of cow waste products is slowest in winter.
  (i)   Suggest and explain why the breakdown of waste products is slowest in winter. [2]
  (ii) Suggest and explain how the generator could be adapted so that it would work quicker in winter with the minimum running cost. [3]

(NEAB, Tier Q, June 1995)

9. (a) Describe how **one** method of producing ethanol-based fuel meets each of the requirements for an industrial process:
  (i)   Inexpensive raw materials. [1]
  (ii) The right organism or enzyme. [1]
  (iii) A suitable environment to give high yields. [1]
(b) Read the following passage.

An enzyme implant has successfully reduced the level of particles of the fatty substance, cholesterol, in the blood of rabbits by 40% within 70 minutes. Scientists have developed a way of implanting the enzyme PLA2 into the body without affecting the cholesterol needed in cell membranes. The enzyme is immobilised inside thin hollow fibres. Pores in the walls of the fibre are large enough for cholesterol particles to diffuse through, but too small for blood cells to enter. The enzyme breaks down the cholesterol, and the products are rapidly taken up by liver cells and removed from the bloodstream.

The scientists are cautious about using enzyme therapy in humans. 'We need to know exactly what happens to the products from the cholesterol in the body', says the head of the laboratory that developed the technique. 'Several drugs already on the market can safely be used to lower cholesterol levels. However an implant of the immobilised enzyme PLA2 could be easily inserted and could last for years.'

  (i)   Explain the advantage of lowering the level of the fatty substance, cholesterol, in the blood. [2]
  (ii) Suggest how the enzyme might be immobilised inside the fibres. [2]
  (iii) Suggest why it is an advantage to immobilise the enzyme inside hollow fibres. [2]
  (iv) The enzyme PLA2 occurs naturally in humans. Explain why the enzyme could not be used as an implant if it did not occur naturally in the human body. [2]

(NEAB, Tier R, June 1996)

10. The diagram illustrates the stages in the treatment of sewage using a trickle filter.

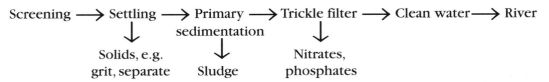

Screening ⟶ Settling ⟶ Primary ⟶ Trickle filter ⟶ Clean water ⟶ River
            ↓   sedimentation   ↓
Solids, e.g.   ↓   Nitrates,
grit, separate   Sludge   phosphates

(a) Describe as fully as you can what happens to the liquid sewage in the trickle filter. [5]

(b) Samples of liquid effluent are used to assess the effectiveness of a sewage works. For each test, one litre of liquid effluent is kept at 20 °C for 5 days. The volume of oxygen consumed by the effluent in this time is measured.

The table shows some results of testing two different methods of sewage treatment.

	Volume of oxygen consumed (mg per litre)
Raw sewage	300
Effluent from trickle filter	30
Effluent from activated sludge	12

    (i) Calculate the percentage by which each method of treatment reduces the volume of oxygen consumed. [2]

    (ii) Explain why the volume of oxygen consumed is much reduced after the sewage has passed through the trickle filter. [3]

    (iii) Explain why the activated sludge treatment is more effective than the trickle filter. [2]

(c) The sludge that settles from the primary sedimentation tanks may be used as a source of biogas.

    (i) Name the principal gas found in biogas. [1]

    (ii) Describe how biogas is produced. [2]

(NEAB, Tier H, June 1997)

11. The diagram below shows one type of sewage treatment works.

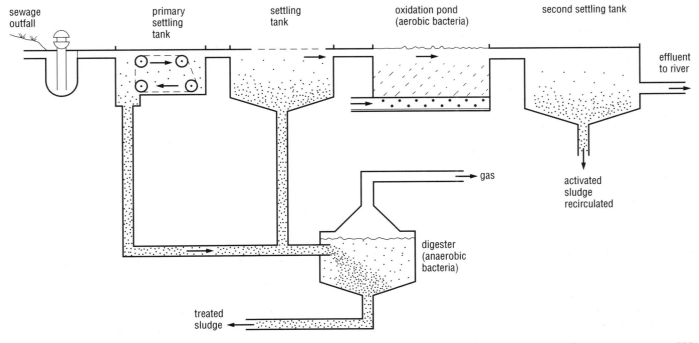

(a) Describe the part played by microorganisms in this type of sewage treatment works. [3]

(b) What is meant by the term **anaerobic**? [1]

(c) Name **one** gas produced by the microorganisms in the digester. [1]

(d) Why is it important to treat sewage before it is pumped into the river? [3]

(London, Higher, Specimen)

Answers to examination questions

Section 1

1 a) Feeding, respiration, reproduction, movement, excretion, sensitivity.
   b) Light, chlorophyll, carbon dioxide
2 Plant cells have cellulose cell walls, chloroplasts, permanent cell vacuoles; animal cells have none of these.
3 a) **A**, Cell wall, gives rigidity, support to the cell.
      B, Nucleus, controls the activities of the cell, contains the genetic information of the cell.
      C, Cytoplasm, chemical reactions of the cell take place here.
   b) *Similarities:* both have a nucleus, cytoplasm and cell membrane, and both carry out respiration.
      Differences: plant cells have a cell wall, vacuole and chloroplasts; animal cells do not.
4 a) Nucleus.
   b) i) Genes/chromosomes.
      ii) It determines the baby's characteristics, e.g. hair colour.
   c) It allows the sperm to swim towards the egg.
   d) i) Cellulose; active transport/diffusion.
      ii) They create a large surface area.
5 a) $(52 + 54 + 56 + 54 + 55) \div 5 = 271 \div 5 = 54.2$ mm.
   b) Cylinders in water: the cells have a lower concentration of water molecules than the surrounding solution, water will pass in by osmosis, therefore the cells will increase in size (length). Cylinders in sugar solution: the cells have a higher concentration of water molecules than the surrounding solution, water will leave the potato cells, therefore the cells will decrease in size (length).
   c) Their mass, diameter, volume flexibility could have been measured.

6

Meiosis	Mitosis
✓	✓
✓	
	✓
✓	
✓	
✓	✓
✓	✓

7 A, G, D, F, E, C and B.
8 a) Nucleus, chromosomes, genes. Tissues, organs, organisms.
   b) Controls movement of substances into and out of cell, maintains the shape of the cell, holds the cell together.

Section 2

1 a) Enzymes break down/hydrolyse food molecules.
   b) The digested food must be absorbed; it must diffuse or move by active transport into the blood capillaries of the villi.
   c) Glucose is used in the process of respiration; to produce energy.
2 a) i) 21 g
      ii) The rest is water.
   b)

	More than tomato soup	About the same as tomato soup	Less than tomato soup
Protein	✓		
Carbohydrate			✓
Fat	✓		

   c) i) Needed to make new cells; for growth; to make enzymes.
      ii) Needed to provide energy.
      iii) Needed to provide energy; make new cell membranes; for insulation.
   d) i) Stomach.
      ii) Large intestine.
      iii) Small intestine (ileum).
      iv) Anus.
   e) Reabsorbtion of water.
3 a) **A**, right atrium; **B**, right ventricle.
   b) Blood enters right atrium; right atrium then contracts; blood flows through the tricuspid valve into the right ventricle; the ventricle contracts; blood flows through the semilunar valve into the pulmonary artery and into the lungs.
      Blood returns to the left atrium in the pulmonary vein; the left atrium contracts; blood flows through the bicuspid valve into the left ventricle; the ventricle contracts; blood flows through the semilunar valve into the aorta.
4 a) Large surface area; thin walls; moist surface; good blood supply.
   b) i) Made in all cells, in the mitochondria.
      ii) Respiration.
   c) Receptors in aorta, carotid artery and brain; breathing/ventilation; fall/decrease; negative feedback.
5 a) i) More oxygen is needed by the muscle cells for respiration to provide the energy (ATP) for contraction.
      ii) Breathing rate must increase; more oxygen must be taken up by gaseous exchange; this must be carried to the muscles.
      iii) This will increase blood flow to the muscles.
      iv) Oxygen; carbon dioxide; water.
      v) Lactic acid.

b) During exercise an oxygen debt is built up; due to anaerobic respiration; lactic acid produced must be broken down using oxygen.

6 a) The starch must be broken down by enzymes, into sugar/glucose.

b) i) The stored carbohydrate would be broken down into sugars and used in the cells for respiration, producing energy, which is needed for muscle contraction.

ii) Diet A is the best, because it provides the greatest/higher amount/proportion of stored carbohydrate in muscles.

7 a) Sprinters can run faster in the first races; however, long-distance runners were better able to maintain their speeds in the races, their speeds are more consistent.

b) It is still rising; lactic acid still building up; lactic acid is passing into blood from the muscle.

c) It would fall; it is taken to the liver and broken down using oxygen.

d) Long-distance runners can continue to respire aerobically for longer because they have greater oxygen uptake; therefore they do not respire anaerobically as soon and so produce less lactic acid.

8 a) **A**, the cornea; **B**, the optic nerve.

b) **C** should point to the lens.

c) The circular muscles of the iris contract, radial muscles relax, causing the pupil to become smaller.

d) Cones and rods. Cones produce precise detailed images in colour in bright lights. Rods produce less detailed images in black and white but allow us to see in dim light.

e) **X**, a motor neurone; **Y**, a sensory neurone.

f) i) A synapse, synaptic gap.

ii) The pre-synaptic neurone produces a neurotransmitter substance, which diffuses across the gap, stimulating the next neurone (the post-synaptic neurone).

9 Knee jerk, pupil size reflex, blinking, removing hand from hot object, etc. The answer should mention the appropriate stimulus, e.g. light; stimulating a receptor, e.g. eye; which sends an impulse to the central nervous system, i.e. the coordinator; which sends an impulse to an effector, e.g. muscles of the iris; which produces a response, e.g. muscles of the iris contract to change pupil size.

10 a) i) To control the level of sugar in their blood; to reduce blood sugar when it rises; diabetics produce no insulin or too little insulin; their pancreas is not working.

ii) If there is too much insulin then more of the blood sugar (glucose) will be converted into glycogen in the liver.

iii) During exercise the muscles use more glucose; the glucose is needed for extra respiration to provide more energy for exercise.

b) Because sugar is a smaller/more soluble molecule; it can be more easily and therefore more quickly absorbed than starch, which must be digested first.

c) If blood sugar falls too low then the pancreas secretes glucagon; this causes more glycogen to be converted into glucose.

d) A high blood sugar level causes more insulin to be produced; insulin causes blood sugar levels to fall; falling blood sugar causes production of insulin to be reduced; therefore blood sugar levels only vary slightly.

11 a) Day 17/18, and day 28/1.

b) Build-up of oestrogen causes an increase in the thickness of the lining of the uterus.

c) i) Progesterone.

ii) The corpus luteum of the ovary.

iii) Menstruation.

iv) Pregnancy.

12 a) i) They are hormones.

ii) They are carried in the blood.

b) i) As production of FSH increases so does production of oestrogen; high levels of oestrogen cause production of FSH to be reduced.

ii) Levels of FSH will remain high, therefore it is more likely that an egg will mature and be released.

13 a) The cortex.

b) Because the glucose is selectively reabsorbed.

c) Urine.

d) In Bowman's capsule.

14 a) The blood plasma is filtered in Bowman's capsule. The filtrate then trickles through the rest of the tubule where selective reabsorption takes place; all the glucose and excess water and mineral ions are reabsorbed.

b) i) The fluid would contain no/less urea.

ii) The fluid would contain the same concentration of glucose and be at the same temperature.

15 a) Blood plasma is filtered; water is reabsorbed in the tubule; amount reabsorbed depends on ADH; if there is a low water content in the blood ADH will be produced; this increases the permeability of the tubule; more water is reabsorbed; a small volume of concentrated urine is produced; if water concentration is high the reverse will happen.

b) i) Advantages include: permanent cure; return to normal lifestyle and diet; more convenient than having to use the machine; cheaper in the long term.

ii) Disadvantages include: risk of rejection; not enough donor organs available; risk during the surgery (operation); risk of infection if immunosuppressant drugs are used.

16 If body temperature is too high then skin blood capillaries dilate (vasodilation); blood flow increases; sweat is released from the sweat glands and evaporates, cooling the skin surface; hair erector muscles relax so less air is trapped, reducing insulation; so more heat is lost.

If body temperature is too low then skin blood capillaries narrow (vasoconstriction); blood flow is reduced so less heat is lost; no sweat is produced; hair erector muscles contract and hair is raised; insulating layer of air is trapped; muscles contract involuntarily (shivering) to produce heat.

17 a) i) **A**, uterus; **B**, oviduct; **C**, ovary; **D**, cervix; **E**, vagina.
   ii) Fertilisation.
   iii) The fertilised egg implants itself in the wall of the uterus.

b) i) It acts as a shock absorber, and it helps to prevent temperature changes/fluctuations.
   ii) The fetus is lying head down; the fetus' head is pressing down on the cervix/its head is low down in the pelvis.
   iii) The cervix must dilate/stretch to allow the fetus to pass through. The uterus has muscles which must contract to push the fetus out through the cervix.

c) i) Sterilisation = surgical; intra-uterine device = mechanical; rhythm method = natural.
   ii) It is permanent/one treatment; it has no side-effects.

18 a) i) In the placenta, oxygen and food molecules diffuse into the fetal blood; carbon dioxide and waste is removed from the fetal blood.
   ii) The ensure that there is rapid/efficient diffusion.
   iii) To prevent most microorganisms reaching the fetus; to prevent cells from the fetus entering the mother's blood.

b) i) The lining of the uterus is being lost with a small volume of blood.
   ii) The lining becomes thicker.
   iii) On the day of ovulation the body temperature rises from 36.5 to 36.9 °C; an egg is being released from the ovary.
   iv) By taking her temperature every day for several months, the woman can work out which day of her cycle ovulation takes place; she can avoid intercourse on and around that day.
   v) In some months the day of ovulation may change/cycle may become irregular; it may not be possible to avoid intercourse, and if so there is nothing to prevent fertilisation.

c) i) FSH.
   ii) FSH may stimulate the development of more than one egg.
   iii) Eggs are removed from the woman's ovary directly via a fine tube inserted through the body wall; this by-passes the blockage; the eggs are then fertilised outside, a microscope is used to observe this; the fertilised eggs are then introduced into the uterus directly via the cervix.

19 a) i) **C**.
   ii) **B**.
   iii) **D**.
   iv) **A**.

b) **D**, the cartilage.

c) i) Spongy bone is lighter so the skeleton is not too heavy; it allows some compression; it absorbs shock.
   ii) Red blood cells, white blood cells and platelets are made here.

20 a) Synovial fluid.

b) i) Muscle **A**, the biceps.
   ii) Because as the muscles contract they become shorter, so the muscle pulls on the radius; the muscle is fixed at the shoulder blade, which does not move.

c) The tendons are strong so they keep the muscles firmly attached to bone; they are inelastic so when the muscle contracts the bones move.
   Ligaments are strong so they keep the bones together, prevent them separating; they allow a little movement of the joint as they are slightly elastic.

21 a) Viruses.

b) Bacteria.

c) Fungi.

22 a) Bacterium has flagella, protozoan does not; bacterium has no nucleus, protozoan has one; bacterium has no nuclear membrane, protozoan has; bacterium has no contractile vacuole, protozoan has; bacterium has no projections (pseudopodia), protozoan has; bacterium has a cell wall, protozoan does not.

b) i) Has branching threads/strands/hyphae.
   ii) Contact with/pick up spores from places such as swimming pools, changing room floors; contact with an infected person or their clothes, towels, combs etc.; contact with an infected animal such as a cat or dog.

c) Virus is carried in droplets of mucus that are spread when people cough and sneeze.

23 a) 20 °C.

b) Keep refrigerated, keep cool/below 7 °C.

c) The time milk stays fresh decreases as storage temperature increases; each 10 °C rise in temperature has a greater effect on reduction in stay-fresh time.

24 Landfill site:
Advantages: cheap, land such as old quarry sites can be reclaimed.
Disadvantages: the sites can be unsightly/smelly; they can attract vermin such as rats; they can attract vectors of disease; they destroy natural habitats as more and more are needed; they can produce methane.
Incineration:
Advantages: pests/vermin/vectors of disease not attracted; can be used to generate energy/heat; does not require a lot of land.
Disadvantages: they are expensive to build; they need fuel to burn the waste; they may produce toxic fumes; as not all waste can be burned, some kind of sorting process is needed.

25 a) i) 3.7 + 2.1 + 2.4 = 8.2%.
   ii) 8.2 ÷ 100 × 180 = 14.7/14.8/15.

b) Alcohol has a direct effect on the brain/nervous system; it changes the chemical processes taking place; it is a depressant; it slows down reactions.

26 a) Microorganisms have proteins on their surface, called antigens; these are detected/recognised as foreign by the white blood cells; phagocytes may ingest the microorganism and break it down; lymphocytes may produce antibodies; these can be released into the plasma; the antibodies will bind to/attack the microorganism/antigen; in some cases phagocytes engulf and destroy the antibody-coated antigen.

b) i) Weakened bacteria are used to ensure that the patient does not develop the disease.

ii) Dead bacteria would not multiply and so would not stimulate an immune response/production of lymphocytes.

iii) The person will remain immune because memory cells/lymphocytes have been made; the person has an immunological memory of the disease; so if the person is exposed to TB, antibodies will be made very quickly/a secondary response is produced.

c) The serum contains ready-made antibodies against tetanus these can immediately destroy the tetanus organism; but the antibodies will be destroyed in the patient who will not be able to make more.

27 a) i) An antigen is a foreign protein which stimulates an immune response.

ii) The surface/coat of the virus carries the antigen.

b) i) Different time scales are used so that the effect of HIV can be shown for the first few weeks after infection and long term.

ii) As the HIV antigen increases the number of T helper cells decreases.

iii) When the number of T helper cells is low symptoms of disease will be seen; this is because the immune response will be depressed/weaker; antibody production will be low; the person will be at risk from infectious diseases; the person may die of a disease we can normally recover from; diseases such as pneumonia become fatal.

c) i) A secondary response is the rapid response produced when the body meets an antigen it has met before.

ii) The secondary response is possible because the body has an immunological memory/memory cells for that specific antigen.

iii) It produces rapid destruction of the antigen before there are any disease symptoms; it means we do not show symptoms of disease more than once.

28 a) Ingest microorganisms/phagocytosis; produce antitoxins which neutralise the effects of toxins released by the microorganism; produce antibody which destroys the microorganism.

b) Viruses live inside cells, therefore antibiotics cannot attack the virus; the body cell could be destroyed if the antibiotic attacked the virus.

c) i) The foreign microorganism stimulates multiplication of lymphocytes; these produce antibodies and memory lymphocytes.

ii) Use a non-virulent strain; use antigen (protein) separated from the surface of the microorganism; use genetically engineered bacteria to produce antigen molecules (protein); use a chemically modified toxin, a toxoid.

29 The red blood cells of the group **A** blood have **A** antigen on their surface; the plasma of group **B** blood contains antibody **a**; when the antigen **A** meets the **a** antibody then agglutination takes place (the cells clump together).

30 a) **C**, because antiseptic **C** has killed the most bacteria after 24 hours.

b) Antiseptic **A** seems to have had little effect; the bacteria are still growing.

c) The bacteria could multiply and cause tooth decay; could damage the cells of the gums, causing gum disease; gum disease or tooth decay can cause bad breath.

d) Clean/brush teeth; use fluoride toothpaste; use dental floss.

31 *Either:* Clean the surfaces, one section with sodium hypochlorite, one with the detergent; wipe each surface with a separate sterile piece of cotton wool, wipe the surface of two separate agar plates with the cotton wool; cover each agar plate and leave for 24 hours; compare the number of bacteria growing by counting the number of colonies.

Or: Use sterile cotton wool to wipe uncleaned surfaces; transfer the bacteria to two separate agar plates; add a small volume of sodium hypochlorite to one and the same volume of detergent to the other; cover and leave for 24 hours; compare the number of bacteria growing by counting the number of colonies.

Control: An agar plate untreated but kept in the same conditions.

Section 3

1 a) **A**, incisor; **B**, canine; **C**, carnassial.

b) **A**, scraping meat from bones and pulling the meat apart; **B**, killing and holding prey, tearing meat; **C**, cutting meat, crushing bones.

c) i) Jaws move up and down.

ii) Jaws move from side to side and in a circular action.

2 a) Plankton (zoo/phytoplankton).

b) The mollusc is a filter feeder; cilia beat, creating a current of water; the water is taken into the mollusc; the water contains plankton; these are filtered off by the gills/trapped on the gills of the mollusc.

3 a) The animal has strong leg bones; these would be needed to support the body on land.

b) The animal has a streamlined shape, which would make it easier for it to move through water; bones of the feet spread out/form paddle shape, which could make swimming more efficient.

4 a) i) The sternum and keel must be large to allow attachment of large and strong muscles; these muscles are needed for flight and so they must be powerful.

ii) The spaces make the bone lighter/reduce weight of skeleton, but the bone is still strong.

b) Downstroke; downwards; closed flat; lift; upstroke.

5 a) i) The median (dorsal and ventral) fins reduce rolling.

ii) The median (dorsal and ventral) fins reduce yawing.

iii) The pectoral and pelvic fins reduce pitching.

b) Muscle blocks on either side of the vertebral column work antagonistically (one contracts whilst the other relaxes); when the muscles contract the vertebral column is bent; alternate contraction and relaxing moves tail from side to side; waves of contraction pass down the fish; movement of the tail creates a backthrust.

6 a) A parasite is an organism that takes its food from a host organism; the host is always harmed; it is a special form of symbiosis.

b) It has suckers; it has a flattened body/large surface area; it lacks a means of locomotion.

Section 4

1 a) In the cupboard there would be no light; light is needed for photosynthesis, therefore there would be no photosynthesis; all the starch would be used up by the plant.

b) i) Chlorophyll.

ii) Oxygen.

c) P_3 had carbon dioxide, Q_3 did not, therefore starch is present in P_3 but not in Q_3; P_2 had light, Q_2 did not, therefore starch is present in P_2 but not in Q_2.

2 a) The seedlings should be placed in a lightproof container/box which has a single small opening on one side to allow entry of light.

b) i) All the seedlings would grow taller except **B**, which does not grow taller/grows only slightly taller.

ii) **A** grows towards the light; **B** will not grow towards the light; **C** will grow straight; **D** will grow towards the light.

c) The tip or top of the stem/shoot.

d) i) Phototropism.

ii) The auxin/growth-promoting substance is made in the stem/shoot tip; it diffuses down the stem/shoot, but diffuses away from the 'light' side to the 'dark' side so more is present on the dark side, where it stimulates greater cell elongation/expansion and therefore growth.

3 a) i) Poor root growth; purple; smaller leaves.

ii) Death of leaves.

b) i) Nitrogen is needed to make protein; protein is needed for plant growth; with less protein growth will be slower.

ii) Magnesium is needed to make chlorophyll; less chlorophyll means that leaves will become yellow; photosynthesis will be affected.

4 a) The arrows should show the water entering the roots, passing up through the stem and out through the leaves (lower surface).

b) i) Osmosis.

ii) Water passes through a selectively permeable membrane from a region of high water concentration (low solute concentration) to a region of low water concentration (high solute concentration).

c) i) The plant loses water through the leaves by transpiration; the rate of water loss is controlled/determined by the size or number of stomata present.

ii) Excess water loss will lead to wilting/dehydration; this will lead to a reduced rate of photosynthesis.

5 a) i) Plant cells have strong cellulose cell walls; the cells contain water, which creates a pressure on the cell walls: the cells are turgid; there is a series of veins containing xylem and phloem throughout the leaf.

ii) Water is lost by evaporation/transpiration; turgor is lost/cells become plasmolysed.

b) i) Those plants closest to low water level have the highest salt concentration; this means that they do not lose water by osmosis and can still take it in because the concentration of water inside the plant is still less than outside; plants further up the shore have a lower salt concentration.

ii) Having small leaves means the surface area of the leaves is less/there would be fewer stomata; this would reduce the rate of evaporation/water loss from the leaves. If the stomata are deep-set there will be reduced air movement, increased humidity/moisture around the stomata; this lowers the rate of evaporation because there is slower diffusion/a less steep diffusion gradient.

c) i) Mineral ions are taken up by active uptake/transport against a concentration gradient; this requires energy; there is some uptake by diffusion.

ii) If the soil is waterlogged the roots will be short of oxygen; this reduces the rate of respiration and therefore energy release needed for active transport.

6 a) **A**, stigma; **B**, ovule.

b) Draw a line from the pollen grain down the style into the ovary and through the micropyle (gap).

c) Fertilisation.

Section 5

1 a) DNA is a double helix, the bases on the nucleotides always pairing A and T, C and G.

b) Watson and Crick.

c) Strand with A–C–A–G.

2 a) i) Between stage 2 and 3.

ii) A change in the structure of a gene or chromosome or a change in chromosome number.

b) i) UV light, radiation/radioactivity, chemicals such as benzene and mustard gas, chemicals from cigarettes.

ii) If the mutation gives the organism a selective advantage which allows it to compete more successfully and survive, the organism will pass on the mutant gene to its offspring; other organisms which do not have the gene are less likely to survive.

3 a) To remove the pollen-producing anthers to prevent self-fertilisation.

b) To prevent any other pollen reaching the stigmas.

c) Because the white allele is dominant to the yellow allele.

d) Either mutation had occurred, or the white flower in that cross was a hybrid.

e) i) Genotypes: **Ff**   **ff**

Gametes: Ⓕ and ⓕ   all ⓕ

	F	f
f	Ff	ff

Offspring: **Ff** white   **ff** yellow

ii) Approximately 30.

4 a)   XY
X and X   X and Y
XX   XY

b) **G**, 50%; **H**, 0%.
Huntingdon's chorea is dominant, therefore **C** must have the genotype *hh*; **D** must be *Hh* because his father is normal, therefore:

hh   ×   *Hh*
all *h*   *H* and *h*

	H	h
h	Hh	hh

The parents of **H** are both *hh*, as they do not have Huntingdon's chorea; therefore there is no chance of **H** having the disease.

5 a)

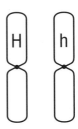

b) i) Mr Smith is $X^h Y$ and Mrs Smith is $X^H X^h$; this is because Julie is a haemophiliac and therefore $X^h X^h$; she must have received a haemophilia allele from both parents.

ii) None, as a haemophiliac female would have the genotype $X^h X^h$, but Peter is normal and therefore does not have a haemophilia allele to pass on.

6 a) Sex-linked.

b) *N* represents the allele for normal sight and *n* the colour-blindness allele.

c) Tom is $X^n Y$ and Rory is $X^N Y$.

d) $X^N X^n$; Tom is colour-blind and he receives his X chromosome from his mother, so this must carry an *n* allele; Susan is not colour-blind and therefore her other X chromosome must carry an *N* allele.

e) Haemophilia is a disease in which blood cannot clot and therefore haemophiliacs may die before having children; colour-blindness is not life threatening.

7 a) Members of the same species are able to breed together to produce fertile offspring.

b) Select small parents and allow them to breed; select the smallest dogs from the litter; repeat the process over several generations.

8 a) The allele may have arisen due to mutation.

b) It will fall; normal borers are less likely to survive but resistant ones are more likely, therefore they will pass on the resistance allele.

c) There is much inbreeding; if this is between two heterozygotes some of the offspring will be homozygous; if two homozygous recessive ones breed then all the offspring will be resistant.

d) i) DNA.
ii) The DNA is made up of nucleotides with bases arranged in a specific sequence; it is the sequence of these nucleotide bases that controls the assembly of amino acids in sequence to make a protein.

e) The gene for CFTR is removed/cut out using special enzymes (restriction enzymes); this gene is then inserted into a bacterium which is then cultured up; the bacterium will produce the CFTR.

9 a) The fossil bird has a long tail, the modern bird does not; the fossil bird's rib-cage is less robust/has smaller bones; the modern bird has a large flat keel/sternum bone, the fossil bird does not.

b) i) This makes the skeleton lighter, therefore flight is easier.
ii) Mutations would produce new alleles, which would produce slightly larger air spaces; this was a selective advantage to these birds and perhaps they escaped predators more easily; they were more likely to survive to pass on their mutant alleles; this process would be repeated over many generations.

10 a) Discontinuous.

b) i) In smoke-polluted woodland it is a selective advantage to be melanic, because melanic forms are less likely to be eaten by predators; therefore the melanic forms are more likely to survive to reproduce and pass on their genes.
ii) The population of melanic forms would decline/fall.

11 a) To produce a larger animal; the Large White does not have tusks so it is safer to farm.

b) They may produce more meat; they may be more resistant to disease.

12 In order down the list: **E**; **D**; **A**; **B**; **C**.

13 a) 75/5 = 15 mm.

b) Roots; specialised vascular tissue.

c) No flower and seed production in pteridophytes or bryophytes.

Section 6

1 a) **A**.

b) **C**.

c) **B**.

d) **D**.

2 a) i) India.
   ii) Britain.
   iii) Sweden.

b) A shortage of food/famine; lack of suitable housing/overcrowding; increasing risk of infectious disease; shortage/lack of jobs; shortage of hospitals/schools etc.

3 a) i) Removal of hedges; draining of the marshland; more farm buildings; removal of trees; larger fields.
   ii) There would be fewer wild animals because there are fewer habitats/fewer different types of habitat, for example, marshes and hedges have been removed.

b) i) The manure is broken down by saprophytic bacteria, forming ammonium compounds; the ammonium compounds are converted to nitrite and then nitrate by nitrifying bacteria.
   ii) The plants will grow better/larger, leading to a larger crop/yield; therefore there will be a greater profit; the farmer will save money since he will not have to buy fertiliser.

c) These pesticides will persist in the environment where they may kill wildlife/beneficial species; they may also accumulate in food chains and eventually be found in human food.

4 a) Glucose; water.

b) i) 100 billion + 104 billion = 204 billion tonnes.
   ii) $100 \div 204 \times 100 = 49\%$.

c) The warm water speeds up the process of eutrophication, in which there is a large increase in the number of floating algae; these block out light from other plants; plants die providing food for saprophytic bacteria; these increase in number; they use up the oxygen/BOD increases; fish suffocate.

d) i) There has been a large increase in the human population; there has therefore been a great increase in the demand for consumer goods such as television sets; this has led to an increase in the amount of industry to make these goods; there has also been an increase in the number of vehicles.
   ii) Increased carbon dioxide levels have led to global warming; this is causing the ice caps to melt, changing weather patterns; acid rain is produced when sulphur dioxide and carbon dioxide dissolve in rain water, this kills plants directly or can acidify lakes/soil; it causes aluminium to accumulate, killing plants.
   iii) Removal of trees reduces the amount of photosynthesis; less oxygen will be produced; less carbon dioxide will be removed from the atmosphere; increased levels of carbon dioxide lead to reflected infra-red radiation being trapped in the atmosphere; the Earth's temperature rises; this is the increase in the greenhouse effect. There will also be less transpiration and this will affect rainfall patterns, perhaps leading to drought conditions.

e) Increase in the number of cattle; large areas of rice paddy fields; more landfill sites.

5 a) The chemicals are damaging/weakening the seals' immune systems and therefore they are less able to fight the flu.

b) Plankton; small fish; cod.

c) PCBs are fat-soluble and they will accumulate in fat, including the fat in the seal's milk; baby seals also have a less well-developed immune system than adults.

6 a) Persil/Daz/Bold/Ariel.

b) i) Lux/Ecover/Asda Auto.
   ii) These do not contain enzymes which would be destroyed/denatured by boiling.

c) The production of phosphate uses the heavy metal cadmium; it accumulates in organisms, and reaches toxic levels high up in food chains.

d) The blanket of algae reduces the amount of light reaching other plants; these will die as they cannot photosynthesise; bacteria (saprophytes) will decompose them; the bacteria use oxygen for respiration; animals such as fish will die/suffocate due to oxygen shortage.

e) The use of zeolite, as this has no side-effects/effects on the environment.

f) i) She would be assuming that the virus affected only *Chlorella* and not other species, or that the virus would behave in the sea as it had done in the laboratory.
   ii) The virus might affect other algae; it might mutate and have other effects/attack other species.

7 a) The net reduces movement; this reduces energy wasted in swimming; it reduces the number of fish lost to predators; food is provided which maximises growth; fish do not have to search for food and waste energy.

b) Introduce wrasse, as in the wild they feed on the lice; remove infected fish regularly/as soon as they become infected.

c) If they were fed this frequently less food would be given, so less food would be wasted/not eaten; the number of bacteria feeding on the waste would therefore be low/there would be less decay; therefore oxygen content would remain high.

d) Bacteria feeding on waste would increase; more plants, due to nitrogenous waste from fish; lack of oxygen, due to activity of bacteria, may lead to fewer shellfish.

8 a)

b) i) $44\,000 \div 4\,600\,000 \times 100 = 0.96\%$.
   ii) Some of the light energy is not absorbed; some is re-radiated; some becomes heat energy which is lost due to evaporation/transpiration; some may pass straight through the leaf.

iii) Not all the primary consumer is eaten and digested by the secondary consumer; some of the energy will have been used by the primary consumer for movement; some of the energy will have been lost as heat from the primary consumer; some will have been lost in the waste products of the primary consumer.

c) Saprophytic bacteria break down the proteins into ammonium compounds; these are converted to nitrites and then nitrates by nitrifying bacteria; nitrate is absorbed by the oak tree roots.

9 a) This is because energy is lost at each trophic level because some is used for movement/lost as heat/lost on excretory materials.

b) Tadpole numbers might increase at first, as they have more weeds and plankton to feed on; later their number would fall as the perch and pike have lost a source of food and will take more tadpoles.

c) Fertiliser encourages plankton multiplication; less light is available to other plants; plants and plankton die; decomposition by bacteria uses oxygen; fish will die/suffocate due to lack of oxygen.

10 a) i) Saprophytes (bacteria/fungi).
ii) Ammonium compounds.
iii) Nitrates.
iv) Nitrogen-fixing bacteria.

b) Via their urine and faeces; via decomposition of their dead bodies.

c) i) The plants sprayed with nitrogen-fixing bacteria are larger and have many more leaves.
ii) The bacteria in the clover will fix nitrogen from the air between the soil particles, which is then converted into plant protein; when the plant is ploughed into the soil this nitrogen from the plant protein will be returned to the soil by the action of bacteria.

d) It would be of benefit because the farmer would have to use less fertiliser; this would save money; more importantly, it would reduce damage to the environment due to eutrophication.

11 a) Mussel/caddis larva/mite/diving beetle/loach.

b) At each level not all of the organism is eaten, or digested and absorbed; some is lost in faeces and other excretory material; some is used to produce energy in respiration, which is then used for movement/active transport, etc.; some is lost from the body of the organism as heat; some of the organisms die and are decomposed by saprophytes, so the energy is transferred to the environment.

Section 7

1 a) i) Protein.
ii) DNA/RNA.
iii) Viruses reproduce inside living cells.

b) i) **X** = cell membrane; **Y** = flagellum.

ii) Bacteria are difficult to destroy because they have a fast reproduction rate as they reproduce asexually; they form spores which have a very resistant outer coat that can withstand drying, extreme temperatures and toxins.

2 a) Inoculating loop used; sterilised using a Bunsen flame; bacteria transferred; loop flamed after transfer.

b) Carbohydrate; mineral ions.

3 a) i) The milk used has been pasteurised/sterilised/ boiled/heated to 85–95 °C; sterile containers are used; containers are sealed; yoghurt is placed in refrigerator; lactic acid kills other bacteria.
ii) To ensure that the bacteria in starter culture/ enzymes are not destroyed.

b) Bacteria multiply/reproduce; they ferment the milk sugar, lactose; lactic acid is produced; this causes the milk protein to become solid.

4 a) Mycoprotein contains more fibre and less fat.

b) Microorganisms multiply rapidly; they are easy to grow (they have simple food requirements); they can use cheap/waste materials as food; fermenters take up little space; fermenters can operate all year round (independent of climate); the product is always of the same quality.

5 a) The flask should be autoclaved/sterilised using a pressure cooker/heat-treated.

b) To ensure that only the bacteria that have been introduced are being cultured.

c) Sterilise the inoculating loop in a Bunsen flame; use the sterile loop to obtain a sample of bacteria (from a culture, for example); lift one side of the Petri dish lid and inoculate the agar by passing the loop across the surface of the agar; close the lid and seal.

6 a) i) It has a distinct nucleus.
ii) Without/in the absence of oxygen.
iii) Glucose → ethanol/alcohol + carbon dioxide.

b) i) The pressure would rise/increase.
ii) The airlock allows the carbon dioxide to escape; it prevents pressure becoming too high; it prevents entry of air which might contain bacteria.
iii) Conditions would become aerobic which would allow aerobic respiration to occur; no alcohol would be produced.
iv) Containers must be sterile to ensure no other microorganisms/bacteria are present.

c) Enzymes.

7 a) i) 2.
ii) Rate of bubbling increases as temperature increases; there is a greater increase between 25 and 30 °C than between 15 and 25 °C; rate increases from 2 to 12 bubbles per minute.

b) Rate of bubbling decreases; and then bubbling stops at 55 °C. Above 45 °C the yeast cells are killed; their enzymes are denatured; the yeast's food/glucose supply may have run out; alcohol builds up, stopping fermentation/killing yeast.

c) i) To ensure temperature was stable; to ensure yeast was at the same temperature; to allow new rate to become established.

ii) This made the results more valid/reliable; one reading could be odd/anomalous.

iii) Repeat using the same apparatus but without yeast (or using dead yeast), to show that it is the yeast producing the gas.

8 a) i) Methane.

ii) Anaerobic respiration/fermentation.

iii) The biogas could be used to power generators to make electricity for lighting, or as a fuel for heating.

b) i) In the winter it is colder, therefore enzyme activity in the bacteria is slower, so fermentation is slower.

ii) The fermenter could be insulated; some of the biogas produced could be used to heat the fermenter; biogas could be used to heat water which could be used in a heating coil in the fermenter.

9 a) i) Sugar cane juice; glucose obtained from maize starch.

ii) Yeasts/amylase.

iii) Temperature should be optimum for the enzymes; optimum pH; sterile conditions; plentiful supply of sugar cane juice.

b) i) Lower levels of cholesterol reduce the risk of blocking/narrowing blood vessels; this lowers the risk of heart attacks/heart disease/thrombosis.

ii) The enzyme could be trapped/held inside the fibres; the fibres could be filled with alginate beads containing the enzyme.

iii) The enzyme could not be released/escape into the cells/blood; therefore it cannot damage the cells/blood cells of the rabbit.

iv) If it did not occur naturally it would be recognised as foreign protein/antigen; an immune response would take place/antibodies/antioxins would be produced.

10 a) Liquid sewage trickles over the stones of the filter bed; these stones have a coating/layer/film of microorganisms/bacteria; these digest/break down/feed on the organic matter in the sewage; the organic matter is converted into nitrates and phosphates by the bacteria.

b) i) Trickle filter: $300 - 30 \div 300 \times 100 = 90\%$; activated sludge: $300 - 12 \div 300 \times 100 = 96\%$.

ii) The sewage now contains much less organic matter; therefore there will be fewer bacteria; fewer bacteria will use less oxygen for respiration.

iii) Activated sludge method involves aeration/addition of oxygen; this allows aerobic microbes to feed more actively/digest the sludge more quickly.

c) i) Methane.

ii) Sludge from the sewage is digested by anaerobic bacteria in sludge digesters; they ferment the sludge, producing methane.

11 a) Microorganisms break down/decompose/digest the organic matter in the sewage; their enzymes break it down into harmless carbon dioxide, water and ammonium salts.

b) Oxygen not involved.

c) Methane.

d) Sewage must be treated to remove organic matter which would encourage multiplication of bacteria and therefore cause a decrease in oxygen levels; treatment can remove bacteria which could be harmful; sewage could be toxic.

Answers to quick questions

Section 1.1

1 Respiration, excretion, feeding, growth, reproduction, moving, sensitivity.

2

Cell structure	Animal	Plant
Nucleus	Present	Present
Chloroplast	Absent	Present
Cytoplasm	Present	Present
Cell membrane	Present	Present
Cell wall	Absent	Present
Mitochondria	Present	Present
Vacuole	Absent	Present

3 **a)** Mitochondria.
  b) Nucleus.
  c) Cell membrane.
  d) Chloroplast.
4 A tissue is a group of similar cells carrying out the same function. An example of an animal tissue could be muscle or glandular tissue; an example of a plant tissue could be xylem or photosynthetic tissue.

Section 1.2

1 **a)** Diffusion is the movement of molecules of a liquid or gas from a region of high concentration to a region of lower concentration until both concentrations are the same.
  b) Diffusion occurs when oxygen moves from the alveoli into the blood in the lungs; it occurs when gases leave via the stomata in leaves; it occurs when glucose enters cells from the blood.
2 Osmosis is a special case of diffusion. It is the movement of water from a weak solution (one that has a high water concentration) to a strong solution (one that has a lower water concentration) across a selectively permeable membrane.
3 **a)** A.
  b) The surrounding solution.
4 Turgidity gives support to the plant cells, and therefore to plants. It gives them a firm shape.
5 **a)** Active transport is the movement of molecules from a region of low concentration to a region of higher concentration. It requires energy.
  b) Active transport occurs when minerals are taken up by plant root hair cells; it occurs in the kidney where glucose and other substances are reabsorbed into the blood; it occurs in the gut when glucose is absorbed into the blood in the small intestine.

Section 1.3

1 Chromosomes.
2 **a)** Mitosis.
  b) Meiosis.
3 Mitosis.
4 **a)** 46.
  b) 23.
5 **a)** Meiosis.
  b) Chromosome number is halved.
  c) In the gonads (organs involved in producing gametes, sperm and eggs).

Section 2.1

1 Digestion is needed to break down large, complex, insoluble food molecules into small, simple, soluble ones so that they can be absorbed and used.
2 Enzymes are biological catalysts that speed up chemical reactions both inside and outside cells.
3 High temperatures destroy/denature enzymes. The 3D shape of the active site is distorted so that the substrate molecule can no longer fit.
4 Enzymes have an active site which has a 3D shape, the substrate molecule must fit into the active site for a reaction to take place, it must have the correct shape to fit in.
5 **a)** Stomach, small intestine (duodenum and ileum).
  b) Mouth, small intestine (duodenum and ileum).
6 Glucose, amino acids, fatty acids, glycerol.
7 The villi of the ileum (small intestine). Diffusion and active transport.

Section 2.2

1 **a)** Plasma.
  b) White and red blood cells.
2 Oxygen, carbon dioxide, products of digestion (glucose), urea, hormones, heat, vitamins and minerals, antibodies.
3 They produce chemicals that trigger the clotting process.
4 Oxygen is transported in red blood cells, as oxyhaemoglobin (oxygen combined with haemoglobin).
5 Right and left atria, right and left ventricles.
6 The valves of the heart prevent backflow of blood. The bicuspid valve is between the left atrium and left ventricle, the tricuspid valve is between the right atrium and right ventricle. The semilunar valves are at the base of the aorta and pulmonary artery.
7 Movement of blood through the heart depends on volume and pressure changes on either side of the valves.
8 Arteries carry blood away from the heart, veins carry blood towards the heart; arteries (apart from the pulmonary artery) carry oxygenated blood, veins (apart from the pulmonary vein) carry deoxygenated blood; in arteries blood flows under high pressure in pulses, in veins blood flows under low pressure smoothly; valves are absent from

arteries but present in veins; artery walls are thicker with more elastic and muscle tissue than vein walls; veins have larger lumens than arteries.

9 They form a vast network of vessels with walls that are only one cell thick (very thin).

10 a) The vena cava and pulmonary vein.

b) The aorta and pulmonary artery.

Section 2.3

1 Mucus traps dust and microbes which enter through the mouth and nose, the cilia beat to move the mucus up to the throat where it is swallowed.

2 a) Pulmonary artery.

b) Pulmonary vein.

3 They are lubricated and they allow the lungs to expand freely/easily.

4 The exchange of oxygen and carbon dioxide; it occurs between the alveoli and the blood and between the blood and body cells.

5 The concentration of oxygen is higher in the alveoli than in the blood, so oxygen diffuses along a diffusion gradient into the blood. The concentration of carbon dioxide is higher in the blood than in the alveoli, so carbon dioxide follows the reverse route.

6 Large surface area, thin walls, moist, have an excellent blood supply.

7 The intercostal and diaphragm muscles contract, the ribs move up and out, the diaphragm flattens, the volume of the chest/thorax increases, the pressure in the lungs falls below atmospheric pressure and air is drawn in.

8 a) glucose + oxygen $\rightarrow$ carbon dioxide + water + energy

b) $C_6H_{12}O_6 + 6O_2 \rightarrow 6CO_2 + 6H_2O$ + energy

9 In the mitochondria.

10 ATP.

11 It does not use oxygen; it produces less energy; it takes place in the cytoplasm/mitochondria not involved; breakdown of glucose is incomplete.

12 It takes place in the cytoplasm.

13 Alcohol, carbon dioxide and energy.

14 During vigorous exercise, when insufficient oxygen is available.

15 Glucose $\rightarrow$ lactic acid + energy.

16 This is the extra oxygen needed to get rid of the lactic acid produced in anaerobic respiration.

Section 2.4

1 Central and peripheral nervous system.

2 Motor, sensory and relay/intermediate.

3 Synapse.

4 By the release of a neurotransmitter substance.

5 The stimulus, light, is detected by light receptors in the retina of the eye; impulses pass along sensory neurones to the brain/coordinator; impulses pass along motor neurones

to the muscles of the iris, the effectors; these contract changing the size of the pupil.

6

Light	Eye
Sound	Ear
Chemicals	Taste buds in tongue
Pressure/touch	Mechanical receptors

7 a) Light is refracted/bent here.

b) Protection and to maintain the shape of the eye.

c) Controls the amount of light entering the eye.

d) Refracts light/focuses light on to the retina.

e) Light-sensitive cells here detect light.

8 a) Short and fat (more rounded).

b) Long and thin. Contraction and relaxation of the ciliary muscles changes the tension of the suspensory ligaments.

9 Radial and circular. When the radial muscles contract (and the circular muscles relax) the pupil gets larger. When the circular muscles contract (and the radial muscles relax) the pupil gets smaller.

10 Cones produce detailed images in colour, rods produce less detailed images in black and white.

11 a) Inability to see distant objects clearly; corrected by using a diverging lens.

b) Inability to see nearby objects clearly; corrected by using a converging lens.

Section 2.5

1 A chemical secreted into the blood by an endocrine gland; it has its effect on target tissues or organs.

2 Pituitary.

3 Pancreas.

4 Insulin is secreted; it causes glucose to be converted into glycogen in the liver.

5 Insulin secretion stops and glucagon is secreted; it causes glycogen to be converted into glucose in the liver.

6 Inability to make any or enough insulin; control of diet and the injection of insulin.

7 FSH is produced by the pituitary; this causes the ovary to secrete oestrogen and the testes to secrete testosterone. These control the development of secondary sexual characteristics.

8 Levels rise because FSH stimulates the ovary to produce oestrogen.

9 Ovulation; LH from the pituitary.

10 Progesterone.

11 To stimulate development of eggs in the ovary.

12 Because high levels of oestrogen in the blood inhibits further egg development.

13 Adrenalin.

14 Increases heart rate, diverts blood to the muscles, so more oxygen is delivered to the muscles.

Section 2.6

1 Maintenance of a constant internal environment.
2 Increase or decrease in breathing/ventilation rate; changes are detected by special receptors in the aorta, the carotid artery and the brain itself.
3 Urea is made in the liver and is the product of deamination of surplus amino acids.
4 It takes place in Bowman's capsule; the liquid (plasma) in the blood is forced from the blood capillaries of the glomerulus into Bowman's capsule; a filtrate containing water, urea and other dissolved molecules, such as glucose is produced.
5 It is the reabsorption of valuable substances from the filtrate into the blood in the surrounding blood capillaries; it takes place along the length of the tubule/nephron.
6 The blood leaving the kidney will contain virtually no urea, less water, less salt.
7 Antidiuretic hormone; made in the pituitary; increases the permeability of the tubule to water so that more water can be reabsorbed from the filtrate if necessary.
8 A greater volume of less concentrated urine will be produced. This is because little ADH is secreted, so less water is reabsorbed in the tubule.
9 Low water concentration in the blood results in increased secretion of ADH; when water concentration has returned to normal ADH secretion is reduced.
10 Using a kidney dialysis machine, or having a kidney transplant.
11 Approximately 37 °C. Any change will affect enzyme activity.
12 Vasoconstriction; hair/fur is raised due to contraction of hair erector muscles; shivering/involuntary contraction of skeletal muscles; sweating stops; increased metabolic rate.
13 Vasodilation; hair/fur lies flat due to relaxation of hair erector muscles; sweating; decreased metabolic rate.
14 They will suffer from the effects of hypothermia as enzyme activity will slow down.

Section 2.7

1 a) To produce sperm and testosterone.
   b) To carry sperm from the testes to the urethra.
2 In the oviduct.
3 In the uterus.
4 To allow exchange of oxygen, glucose, carbon dioxide and urea between the blood of the mother and that of the fetus.
5 Alcohol, carbon monoxide, paracetamol, rubella (German measles) virus, HIV.
6 a) A single zygote divides into two separate portions, both of which develop.
   b) Two eggs are fertilised by two sperm.
7 FSH and LH.
8 They contain oestrogen and progesterone, which inhibit egg production.
9 Gonorrhoea, HIV.

Section 2.8

1 It provides support, a framework and protection, and blood cells are made in bone marrow.
2 Calcium carbonate, calcium and magnesium phosphate.
3 Cartilage.
4 To produce both red and white blood cells.
5 It reduces wear and tear on the bones at a joint; it allows the bones to move more freely.
6 Fixed joints: joints between plates of the skull, and between bones of the pelvic girdle; freely movable joints: elbow, hip, knee.
7 In a freely movable joint, synovial fluid acts as a lubricant to reduce friction and allow free movement.
8 They work in groups or pairs in which one muscle contracts when the other relaxes.
9 a) They are both very strong.
   b) Ligaments are slightly elastic but tendons are inelastic; ligaments join bone to bone, tendons join bone to muscle.
10 In a sprain, ligaments and other tissues are torn; in a dislocation, a bone is forced out of a joint.
11 Rate of both increases; volume of each breath and stroke volume of the heart increase.
12 Pulse rate falls; vital capacity increases; muscles are toned and tendons become supple.

Section 2.9

1 Microorganisms, inherited disease, industrial disease, ageing, lifestyle disease.
2 Viruses, bacteria, fungi, protozoa.
3 Droplet (influenza and TB); contaminated water (cholera); contaminated food (*Salmonella* food poisoning); contact (HIV); via vectors (malaria); unhygienic disposal of household rubbish (Weil's disease).
4 Damage/destruction of cells or the release of toxins.
5 Immunisation (measles, TB, tetanus); elimination of the disease-causing organism or its vector (*Salmonella*, malaria); avoiding contact with the disease-causing organisms or with infected people (HIV and TB); treating the disease in its early stages (TB and meningitis).
6 a) *Salmonella*.
   b) Washing hands, controlling flies and rodents, separating raw and cooked meats, thorough cleaning, thorough cooking of meat, thorough thawing of food, identification of carriers, preventing carriers working in the food industry.
   c) Animals are reared intensively; battery hens, for example, stand on or close to their faeces.
7 Refrigeration (yoghurt and cheese); deep freezing meat; drying (skimmed milk powder, dried fish); osmotic preservation using salt or sugar (jam, bacon); canning or bottling (canned meat such as corned beef, canned vegetables such as peas and beans); irradiation (soft fruit); pasteurisation (milk); ultra-heat treatment (milk).

8 Screening, sedimentation, filtration, chlorination and storage.
9 Skin, mucus and cilia in the respiratory system, acid in the stomach, phagocytosis.
10 Lymphocytes; antibodies or antitoxins.
11 They alter the chemical processes in the body.
12 a) Increased risk of lung cancer, emphysema and bronchitis.
   b) Increased heart rate and blood pressure, leading to irregular heartbeat and increased risk of heart disease.
13 It slows reactions, impairs judgement and may lead to loss of consciousness; in the long term it may lead to brain and liver damage.
14 a) Change in behaviour/hallucination.
   b) Damage to skin, brain, liver and kidneys.
15 Drugs taken by sports people to improve muscle development and performance. Side-effects include damage to liver, increased aggressive behaviour and irregular menstrual cycles.

Section 2.10

1 Penicillin, streptomycin.
2 They prevent the manufacture of cell walls in bacteria, or they destroy the cell membrane of the bacteria.
3 Antibiotic-resistant strains of bacteria have developed.
4 Antigens are proteins found on the surface of cells, they cause an immune response in the bodies of organisms; antibodies are specific proteins that are produced by lymphocytes and will destroy antigens.
5 Lymphocytes (B and T) rapidly divide to produce clones, the clones then produce antibody to destroy the antigen; some of the clones are memory cells.
6 The memory cells, produced on the first exposure to the antigen, can respond very quickly when the same antigen is met again.
7 Our secondary immune response is so fast that the antigen is unable to multiply and produce symptoms.
8 Giving ready-made antibodies such as anti-tetanus antibodies; giving a vaccine containing modified antigen which produces an immune response, as with polio and TB vaccines.
9 From killed organism, from live non-virulent organism, from antigen proteins separated from the organism, from a modified toxin, from antigen produced by genetically engineered bacteria.
10 Side-effects, allergic reactions, in rare cases encephalitis.
11 The antigens on the donor cells are recognised by the recipient's lymphocytes as foreign, and they mount an immune response to destroy the foreign cells.
12 Tissue typing, use of immunosuppressant drugs, irradiation of bone marrow of the recipient.
13 The donor's red blood cells are agglutinated by the recipient's plasma antibodies; this is because the donor red blood cells are recognised as foreign by the recipient.
14 Refer to Table 2.10.2.

Section 3.1

1 Plants, because they are able to manufacture their own organic food molecules.
2 Plant material is difficult to digest, therefore they need special grinding teeth, and also a gut which contains bacteria to digest the cellulose.
3 Herbivores have no canine teeth, while those of carnivores are well developed; incisors may be absent in herbivores but present in carnivores; carnivores have special carnassial teeth formed from premolars and molars, herbivores do not; herbivore jaws move side to side, carnivore jaws move up and down.
4 Mosquito, greenfly (aphids), butterfly, housefly.
5 They filter out microscopic plankton from water.
6 The gills.
7 The dead remains of plants and animals.
8 Release of enzymes on to the food; the digested food is then taken up/absorbed by the organism.
9 Two organisms of different species living together; examples include lichen (alga and fungus), bacteria in the stomachs of cows, nitrogen-fixing bacteria in the root nodules of leguminous plants.
10 In parasitic relationships the host is harmed in some way: the parasite deprives the host of food, damages the host cells or acts as a vector of disease.

Section 3.2

1 Pseudopodia are created and the cytoplasm flows into them.
2 Using cilia or flagella.
3 Pentadactyl plan.
4 The wing is positioned so that air flow over the upper side of the wing is faster than that under the wing. As a result air pressure is greater under the wing, creating lift.
5 The bones are very light; birds have an enlarged breast bone for greater muscle attachment.
6 a) Large flight muscles contract, wing is pulled down, wings are fully outstretched and tilted forward, this gives lift and pushes the air backwards, feathers are closed.
   b) Smaller flight muscles contract, wings are tilted backward, wing is bent at the wrist, feathers are open and the wing is raised.
7 Streamlined, large muscle blocks on either side of the vertebral column, large tail fin, swim bladder; median, pectoral and pelvic fins used to stabilise and steer.
8 As the muscles on one side of the vertebral column contract, the ones on the other side relax.
9 As the tail moves from side to side it creates both backward and sideways thrust; the sideways thrusts to left and right cancel out, leaving only backward thrust.
10 a) To prevent roll and yaw.
   b) To prevent pitch.
11 Hydrostatic skeletons and exoskeletons.
12 The skeletons of land animals are usually more robust; the bones are larger, stronger and usually heavier.

Section 3.3

1 In the early part of the animal's life-cycle it exists in a totally different form from the adult; the tadpole's change into a frog is an example.
2 Eggs are laid on plant leaves because these are the food source of the caterpillars (larvae).
3 Larvae (caterpillars).
4 The caterpillar's cells are broken down and used to form those of the adult.
5 It must take place in water.
6 It is a cluster of frogs' eggs surrounded by layers of jelly (albumin).
7 Tadpole uses external gills, then internal gills and finally lungs, for gas exchange; hindlimbs and then forelimbs emerge from the body; tail shortens and disappears.

Section 4.1

1 $$\text{carbon dioxide} + \text{water} \xrightarrow[\text{chlorophyll}]{\text{light}} \text{glucose} + \text{oxygen}$$

$$6CO_2 + 6H_2O \xrightarrow[\text{chlorophyll}]{\text{light}} C_6H_{12}O_6 + 6O_2$$

2 Light, chlorophyll, carbon dioxide and water.
3 In the chloroplasts of the palisade mesophyll cells of a leaf.
4 Leaves are broad and flat to ensure maximum absorption of light; leaves are thin to reduce the length of the diffusion path for gases; palisade cells have many chloroplasts and are at right angles to the epidermis to ensure maximum light absorption; there are interconnecting air spaces in the spongy mesophyll to allow free movement of gases; stomata are present; xylem and phloem provide an efficient transport system.
5 Up to an optimum, increased light intensity increases rate of photosynthesis; increased carbon dioxide concentration increases rate of photosynthesis; up to an optimum, increased temperature increases rate of photosynthesis.
6 The limiting factor.
7 Using propane or butane burners will increase temperature and concentration of carbon dioxide; the use of artificial lighting.
8 a) Protein manufacture.
   b) Needed for proper functioning of the enzymes involved in respiration and photosynthesis.
   c) Needed for the reactions involved in photosynthesis and respiration.
   d) Production of chlorophyll.
   e) Production of cell walls.
9 At midday the rate of photosynthesis is greater than the rate of respiration and therefore any carbon dioxide produced in respiration is used for photosynthesis. At midnight only respiration is taking place and so carbon dioxide is released.
10 *Positive:* increased crop yield; more plants can be grown per unit area; less land needs to be cultivated.
   Negative: run-off causes eutrophication; nitrate can build up in water supplies.

Section 4.2

1 Water, gravity and light.
2 Auxin.
3 It controls plant cell elongation/expansion.
4 Growth responses of a plant towards or away from a stimulus.
5 Auxin accumulates on the dark (away from the light) side of the shoot. This causes the cells here to enlarge/expand more quickly than those on the light side. Therefore the shoot bends towards the light.
6 They grow in the same direction in which gravity acts, that is, they grow downwards.
7 In rooting powder, to encourage root growth in plant cuttings; to encourage fruit development and prevent fruit fall; to regulate ripening of fruit; to produce fruit growth without the need for fertilisation; as weedkillers.

Section 4.3

1 By osmosis: the concentration of water outside the root is greater than inside so water enters the root across the selectively permeable membrane (cell membrane).
2 The concentration of water would be greater inside the root than outside, therefore water would leave the root cells by osmosis, causing wilting.
3 Xylem.
4 Loss of water from the shoot system of a plant by evaporation of water from moist mesophyll cells.
5 This is because the leaf is so well adapted for gas exchange, with a large surface area of moist mesophyll cells in contact with the atmosphere via the stomata.
6 The shape of the guard cells of the stomata depends on how much water they contain; this determines if the stomata are open or closed. If the guard cells are turgid the stomata are open; if the guard cells are flaccid the stomata are closed.
7 Humidity, temperature, air movement/wind, time of day, altitude.
8 A potometer.
9 Leaves rolled, sunken stomata, reduced leaf surface area, a covering of hairs on leaves, thicker waxy cuticle.
10 The cells are plasmolysed, the cytoplasm and cell wall shrink away from the cell wall.
11 By active transport and diffusion.
12 Phloem.

Section 4.4

1 a) To attract pollinators/insects.
   b) To produce pollen.
   c) To produce ovules (eggs), site of fertilisation.
   d) To produce nectar.
2 The transfer of pollen from the anther of the stamen to the stigma of the carpel of the same or a different flower.
3 Insect-pollinated flowers are large, brightly coloured and produce nectar; wind-pollinated flowers are small, dull and

do not produce nectar. The stamens and stigmas of insect-pollinated flowers are short and found inside the flower; in wind-pollinated flowers they are larger, feathery and hang outside the flower.

4 A pollen tube grows down through the cells of the style and through the micropyle of the ovule. The tube bursts open to release the male gamete.

5 a) Plumule.
  b) Radicle.
  c) Endosperm.

6 Animal: holly, tomato; wind: dandelion, sycamore; explosive: lupin, pansy; water: coconut.

7 Oxygen, water, a suitable temperature.

8 Asexual reproduction, involving one parent.

9 Horizontal runner (stolon) produced, carrying at its tip a bud which can develop into a new plant when it touches the soil.

10 By taking cuttings.

Section 5.1

1 Continuous: extremes of a characteristic with a range of intermediate types. Discontinuous: distinct types with no intermediates.

2 a) Has two sets of chromosomes.
  b) Has only one set of chromosomes, as in a gamete.

3 23 pairs.

4 It is halved.

5 Nucleotides.

6 The double helix unwinds, free nucleotides arrange themselves alongside the exposed bases and pair up A–T and C–G.

7 The sequence of nucleotides on a strand of DNA codes for the assembly of amino acids in the right order to make a specific protein.

8 They have a random mixture of genes from two parents; the zygote will contain pairs of genes, one of each pair coming from each parent; the genes for each characteristic may be different.

9 An alteration in the genetic material of a cell in which the sequence of nucleotides may be changed.

10 UV radiation; X-rays; radiation from radioactive substances; chemicals such as mustard gas or benzene; tar from cigarettes.

Section 5.2

1 Genotype: the genes present in the cells of an organism. Phenotype: how the genes are expressed in an organism; its outward appearance.

2 a) Genes are sequences of DNA that control the development of the characteristics of an organism.
  b) Variations of a gene, for example, the gene for height in pea plants has a tall allele and a short/dwarf allele.

3 A dominant allele will have an effect/express itself in both the homozygous and heterozygous condition. A recessive allele will only have an effect/express itself in the homozygous condition.

4 Having different alleles for the same gene.

5 a) XX.
  b) XY.

6 Diseases inherited via the sex chromosomes, usually the X chromosome. Haemophilia and colour-blindness are examples.

7 Shaking, twitching and mental deterioration.

8 Artificial selection: we select out those animals or plants which show the characteristics we want and allow them to breed. This is repeated over several generations to produce new varieties of organisms.

9 Taking cuttings; tissue culture.

10 The human insulin gene is removed from chromosomes using enzymes and is inserted into the DNA (plasmid ring) of bacteria. The 'daughter' bacteria carry the human gene and produce the insulin.

Section 5.3

1 It suggests that organisms change or evolve over time. Existing organisms have evolved from simpler ancestors, some of which are now extinct.

2 Severe changes in abiotic conditions such as temperature, or changes in biotic factors such as a new predator or disease.

3 The mineralised remains of plants and animals, usually found in rocks.

4 The organisms that are the best adapted to the environment.

5 Over many years populations of bacteria have been exposed to antibiotics. Mutations have occurred which produce resistance to antibiotics. Those individuals that have the mutant allele will survive and pass on the mutant allele, the others will die. As a result whole populations will be antibiotic-resistant.

6 A population of similar organisms which can successfully breed, producing fertile young.

Section 5.4

1 c = stonefly nymph; d = caddisfly larva; e = bloodworm; f = water snail; g = dragonfly nymph.

2 The bryophytes.

3 *Spirogyra*, seaweed such as *Fucus*.

4 Have an exoskeleton and jointed legs, and show cephalisation.

5 Amphibians.

Section 6.1

1 A place/area where an organism lives.

2 A population.

3 All the plant and animal species living together in the same habitat.

4 The community and its environment.

5 Temperature, availability of light, water, oxygen, carbon dioxide, nesting sites, nutrients.

6 Small surface area to volume ratio, thick insulating coats, subcutaneous fat.
7 Their life-cycle can be completed before they would have to compete with other plants (trees, for example) for light, water and so forth.
8 Space, water, light and a supply of minerals.
9 The number of predators depends on the number of prey there are, and the number of prey that survive depends on the number of predators. If the population of prey is high more food is available for the predators and their numbers increase. High predator numbers will mean fewer prey survive, and so on.
10 Food webs would be disturbed, and if existing species could not compete with the new species they could disappear from that area.

Section 6.2

1 Carbon dioxide and methane.
2 The greenhouse gases trap heat (infra-red) energy which is radiated from the Earth's surface. The temperature of the Earth rises, causing melting of the polar ice caps. This can cause a rise in sea levels and also climatic changes.
3 Burning of fossil fuels, deforestation, large herds of cattle (producing methane) and large areas of rice paddy fields.
4 a) Soil is eroded, it is washed into rivers.
  b) Less transpiration leads to less rainfall.
  c) Reduced species diversity.
5 The growing of large areas of a single species of plant. It reduces species diversity, and increases the need to use pesticides as pest problems are greater.
6 Soil crumb structure is destroyed; nitrates accumulate in water supplies; it encourages eutrophication in rivers and lakes.
7 Oxides of nitrogen, sulphur dioxide and carbon dioxide.
8 Direct damage to plants; increased acidity in rivers and lakes, leading to the death of fish as their gills become coated with thick mucus; build-up of aluminium, which is toxic to plants, in soil water.
9 Oxides of nitrogen and CFCs.
10 The concentration of toxin increases at each trophic level. Animals feeding at the end of a food chain may receive a large dose which may kill them or their young.
11 Eutrophication. Nitrate and phosphate in the sewage encourages algal growth; this limits light for other species, leading to their death; this causes a large increase in the population of decomposers; their multiplication and respiration is greater in the warmer water. The water becomes deoxygenated, that is, the BOD increases rapidly.

Section 6.3

1 They are the only organisms able to trap sunlight energy and store it in molecules like starch.
2 Decomposers; they feed on dead, decaying plant and animal remains.
3 a) Plants.
  b) Other animals.
4 Both plants and animals.
5 The direction of flow of energy and matter.
6 The number of organisms decreases but their size increases.
7 Materials are lost via excretion (urine) and egestion of undigested matter (faeces). Some of the energy is used at each level for production of new cells, muscle contraction and energy is used in birds and mammals to maintain a constant body temperature. Some energy is lost as heat to surroundings.
8 Providing optimum conditions, e.g. light, temperature, feeding; control of disease and predators; restricting the movement of animals; use of pesticides to control pests.
9 Warm, moist, conditions with plenty of oxygen.
10 Respiration, burning of fossil fuels and erosion of carbonate rock.
11 Photosynthesis.
12 a) Convert ammonium compounds into nitrite, then nitrate.
  b) Convert plant and animal protein into ammonium compounds.
  c) Convert nitrogen in the air into compounds that the plant can use to make protein.

Section 7.1

1

	Cytoplasm	Nucleus	Chloroplast	Cellulose cell wall
Viruses	–	–	–	–
Bacteria	✓	–	–	–
Yeasts	✓	✓	–	✓
Moulds	✓	✓	–	✓
Algae	✓	✓	✓	✓

2 Carbohydrate, minerals, ions and in some cases vitamins and protein extracts.
3 To kill unwanted bacteria, to ensure you are only growing the bacteria you intended to grow.
4 To discourage the growth of microbes which could be harmful to humans.
5 By binary fission.
6 By producing sporangia which give rise to spores.
7 Hyphae, a mycelium.

Section 7.2

1 *Lactobacillus* bacteria.
2 To kill most bacteria.
3 It is protein obtained by the fermentation of the fungus *Fusarium*.
4 It is low in cholesterol; the microorganisms grow quickly; they use cheap waste products as food; they are easy to handle and grow; they can be grown anywhere in the world at any time in a small area of land; the product is always of the same quality.
5 Ethanol, carbon dioxide and energy.
6 Soy beans, roast and crushed wheat.
7 Sugar cane juices and glucose from maize starch.
8 Mainly methane, with some carbon dioxide.
9 They multiply rapidly, are easy to grow, have simple food requirements and can be genetically engineered to produce new enzymes.

10 Held/fixed into some inert support/carrier, for example alginate beads, hollow fibres or an inert matrix.
11 In detergents; pre-digesting protein in baby food; extracting fruit juice from fruit; converting glucose into fructose for slimming foods; in wound dressings where catalase creates oxygen-rich conditions to prevent gangrene.
12 a) Solid objects and grit are removed.
   b) Solid suspended organic matter settles out to form a sludge, which is pumped to anaerobic digesters.
   c) The liquid from the settlement tanks is pumped, with some sludge containing bacteria and protozoa, into aerated tanks. The microorganisms digest suspended organic solids and absorb dissolved organic matter.
   d) The sludge from the sedimentation tanks is digested by anaerobic bacteria producing biogas. The remaining material can be dried and used as fertiliser.

Glossary

Abiotic factors   Physical and chemical factors in the environment which influence living organisms; for example, light availability.

Absorption   The movement of food, gases or other chemicals into cells or into body fluids.

Active site   Part of an enzyme molecule to which the substrate attaches.

Active transport   Transport of molecules from a region of low concentration to a region of high concentration of those molecules against a concentration gradient.

ADH   Anti-diuretic hormone, produced by the pituitary gland; it increases permeability of collecting ducts of the kidney tubules to water.

Adrenalin   Hormone released by adrenal gland; prepares body for 'action' by increasing heart and breathing rate.

Allele   Different forms of the gene for the same characteristic.

Artificial insemination   Method of introducing sperm into the female reproductive tract by artificial means.

Assimilation   Absorption of substances which are then built into other compounds and become part of the organism.

Autosome   Chromosome not involved in the determination of sex.

Autotroph   Organism able to manufacture its own organic molecules.

Auxin   Growth-promoting substance produced by plants; it is involved in phototropism.

Biochemical oxygen demand (BOD)   The amount of oxygen which must be present in water to provide for the respiration of organisms.

Biomass   Mass of organisms in a community or population or habitat.

Biotic factors   The effect of the living components of the environment on organisms; for example, predation.

Chromosome   Structure made of DNA and protein which carries genetic information.

Clone   A group of organisms with the same genotype; also a group of cells produced by a single parent cell.

Community   All the plant and animal species living together in the same habitat.

Compensation point   Light intensity at which the rate of photosynthesis equals the rate of respiration.

Culture medium   A mixture of carbohydrate, mineral ions and in some cases vitamin and protein extracts on/in which microorganisms can be grown in the laboratory.

Deamination   Removal of amino group from amino acids; takes place in the liver.

Denaturation (denatured)   Destruction of the folded 3D structure of proteins, such as enzymes, so they can no longer function; usually due to extremes of temperature or pH.

Diabetes   A disorder caused by insufficient or non-production of insulin.

Dialysis   Separation of large and small molecules using a selectively permeable membrane.

Diffusion   Movement of particles of gas or liquid from a region of high concentration to a region of low concentration, following a concentration gradient.

Diploid   Having two sets of chromosomes.

Division of labour   Different tissues and organs performing different functions in an organism.

Dominant   An allele that has an effect in either the homozygous or heterozygous condition.

Dormancy   A resting condition; the organism is alive but relatively inactive.

Ecosystem   A community and its environment.

Ectotherm   An animal whose body temperature fluctuates with that of the environment.

Egestion   Removal of waste/faecal matter from the body.

Embryo transplantation   Embryos formed by *in vitro* fertilisation being transferred to the uterus of the mother or another 'surrogate' mother.

Emigration   To move away from an area or habitat.

Emulsification (emulsified)   The process which occurs in the small intestine in which bile breaks down large droplets of fat into smaller ones, creating a larger surface area for enzyme activity.

Endotherm   An animal that maintains/regulates its body temperature independently of that of its surroundings.

Environment   The abiotic and biotic features which together describe a habitat.

Enzyme   Biological catalyst; enzymes speed up the rate of chemical reactions.

Eutrophication   Increase in nutrient content of water; it occurs naturally but is accelerated by run-off of artificial fertilisers, animal waste and sewage.

Etiolation (etiolated)   Rapid growth of plant stems and a yellowing of leaves due to lack of light.

Excretion   Any process by which an organism gets rid of waste metabolic products.

FSH   Follicle-stimulating hormone, produced by the pituitary; causes development of one or more ova.

Feeding   Obtaining or making organic molecules needed to provide an organism with energy.

Gamete   Female or male sex cell.

Gene   Part of a chromosome which controls a particular characteristic of an organism.

Genetically identical   Applied to cells or organisms whose DNA (genetic material) is the same.

Genotype   The genes that the cells of the organism contain.

Glucagon   Hormone produced by the pancreas which causes blood glucose to rise; it stimulates conversion of glycogen to glucose.

Gonads   Specialised organs which produce the sex cells (gametes) and hormones involved in reproduction.

Gonorrhoea   Bacterial disease of genital organs; may cause sterility if untreated.

Growth   Increase in the dry mass of an organism.

Habitat   A place/area where an organism lives.

Haploid   Number of sets of chromosomes in a gamete; for example, one set in human gametes.

Hereditary material   Material passed from one generation to the next.

Heterotroph   Organism unable to make its own organic food molecules; it must rely on plants or other organisms to provide them.

Heterozygous   Having two different alleles for a particular characteristic.

HIV   Human immunodeficiency virus.

Homeostasis   Maintenance of a constant internal environment.

Homozygous   Having two identical alleles for a particular characteristic.

Hormone   Chemical secreted into the blood by an endocrine gland that affects target organs or tissues.

Hyperglycaemia   An abnormally high concentration of glucose in the blood.

Hypermetropia   Commonly known as long sightedness; it causes difficulty in focusing on near objects.

Hyperthermia   An abnormally high body temperature, often called heat stroke; it may lead to coma and death.

Hypoglycaemia   An abnormally low concentration of glucose in the blood.

Hypothalamus   Region of the brain that controls many involuntary responses in the body.

Hypothermia   Fall in body temperature below 35 °C; causes drowsiness, and lowers heart and breathing rates.

Insulin   Hormone produced by the pancreas which causes a reduction in blood sugar by stimulating conversion of glucose to glycogen.

***In vitro* fertilisation**   Fertilisation of mammalian egg outside the body of the female (usually in glassware).

Immigration   To move to an area/habitat.

Ion   An atom or group of atoms that has either lost one or more electrons, making it positively charged (e.g. Na^+) or gained one or more electrons, making it negatively charged (e.g. Cl^-).

Kwashiorkor   Severe malnutrition caused by a diet low in protein.

Lactic acid   Product of anaerobic respiration in muscle during vigorous exercise.

Leukaemia   Type of cancer involving the bone marrow and the production of blood cells.

LH   Luteinising hormone, produced by the pituitary; causes ovulation and promotes secretion of progesterone by the ovary.

Life expectancy   The number of years an organism can expect to live.

Lymph   A fluid formed from blood plasma which returns substances to the blood.

Menstrual cycle   Monthly loss of lining of the uterus which is accompanied by some loss of blood.

Meiosis   Often called reduction division; takes place in the gonads and produces genetically different gametes with half the number of chromosomes of the mother cells.

Metabolism   All the chemical processes that take place inside a living organism.

Mitochondria   Cell organelles in which respiration occurs.

Mitosis   Type of cell division that produces genetically identical cells.

Monoculture   The cultivation of large areas of land using a single species of plant.

Movement   Change of position of part or the whole of an organism.

Multicellular organism   Organism composed of many cells.

Myopia   Often called short sightedness; causes distant objects to appear blurred.

Negative feedback   Any monitored change from normal values which sets in motion mechanisms to return the body to normal.

Oestrogen   Hormone released by the ovary; promotes secondary sexual characteristics and development of uterus lining.

Organ   A group of different tissues, the function of each tissue contributing to the function of the organ.

Organ system   Group of organs forming a system that has a particular function.

Osmosis   Movement of water molecules from a region of high concentration of water molecules to a region of low concentration of water molecules across a selectively permeable membrane.

Ovulation   Release of the mature egg from the ovary.

Oxygen debt   Amount of oxygen required to remove lactic acid from the blood after exercise.

Pathogen   An agent, usually a microorganism, which causes disease.

Peristalsis   Wave of contraction of muscle, for example in the gut; serves to move material from one end of a tube to the other.

Phenotype   An organism's outward appearance; how the genes are expressed in an organism.

Photosynthesis   Process occurring in chloroplasts in which inorganic molecules are built up into organic molecules. It is light dependent.

Plasma   Liquid part of the blood consisting of water with dissolved solutes such as glucose.

Plasmolysis (plasmolysed)   State of a plant cell which has lost too much water; the cytoplasm pulls away from the cell wall as the cell contents shrink.

Pollination   Transfer of pollen from the anther of a flower to the stigma of the same or different flower.

Population   A group of organisms of the same species living in the same area.

Progesterone   Hormone produced by the corpus luteum following ovulation; promotes development and maintenance of the uterus lining.

Recessive   When an allele has an effect only in the homozygous condition.

Reduction division   Meiosis.

Reproduction   Process by which an organism produces more of the same species.

Respiration   Chemical process occurring in all living cells, which releases energy.

Rubella   Virus causing the disease commonly called German measles.

Saprophyte   An organism that obtains its food from dead or decaying organic matter.

Secretion   Production and release from a cell of useful material.

Selectively permeable membrane   Membrane across which only certain molecules can pass.

Sensitivity   To be 'aware' of the environment.

Sex chromosomes   Chromosomes that determine the gender of an organism.

Somatic cells   Body cells of an organism other than gametes.

Species   A group of similar organisms which can successfully reproduce to give rise to living young that are themselves fertile.

Substrate   Chemical on which an enzyme acts.

Synapse   Junction/gap between two neurones.

Testosterone   Hormone responsible for maintaining the testes; in humans it causes development of secondary sexual characteristics.

Tissue   A group of similar cells carrying out the same function.

Tissue fluid   Fluid bathing cells of the body; formed from the blood plasma.

Transpiration   Process by which water is lost from a plant.

Turgid   State of a plant cell when it has absorbed water by osmosis.

Vector   An animal that transfers a particular infectious disease to another organism.

Zygote   A fertilised egg cell.

Index